# Variation and Final Account Procedure

W. Howard Wainwright
and A. A. B. Wood

# Variation and Final Account Procedure

Hutchinson of London

Hutchinson & Co. (Publishers) Ltd
3 Fitzroy Square, London W1P 6JD

London Melbourne Sydney Auckland
Wellington Johannesburg and agencie
throughout the world

First published 1963
Second edition 1970
Third edition 1979
© W. Howard Wainwright 1963, 1970, 1979

Set in VIP Times Roman by
Preface Ltd, Salisbury, Wilts.


Printed in Great Britain by
The Anchor Press Ltd, and bound by
Wm Brendon & Son Ltd, both of
Tiptree, Essex

**British Library Cataloguing in Publication Data**

Wainwright, Walter Howard
   Variation and final account procedure. – 3rd ed.
   1. Building — Estimates
   I. Title        II. Wood, A A B
   692'.8        TH437
ISBN 0 09 133611 2

# Contents

# Appendices

# Foreword

The idea of writing a book on variation and final account procedure has been in my mind for many years now. During my experiences firstly as a quantity surveyor retained by the builder and then as a quantity surveyor with a large Local Authority, constantly meeting and working with other quantity surveyors, I began to realize the diversity of methods used in the industry by surveyors and builders when they are preparing variation and final accounts.

This view has been confirmed during the last few years when as a lecturer in advanced building subjects I have met a large number of part-time students. These students come from quantity surveyors' offices, Local Authorities, and large and small building firms; and in discussion they point out the methods that they are instructed to use in their work.

Most quantity surveyors of my generation have had to pick up their ideas from one another, gradually satisfying themselves that the system they use is correct. Today, however, we cannot afford the luxury of allowing young surveyors and builders a period of fifteen to twenty years in which to arrive at a satisfactory conclusion in this way.

When writing this book I have had to approach each problem strictly from the procedure laid down in the forms of contract; but I have tried to point out also what often happens in practice, and the dangers that can arise.

The text is based upon the JCT and GC/Works/1 forms of contract, and when the procedure in these two standard forms varies this has been explained. The JCT form actually referred to in this book is the 1963 Edition (Revised July 1977). The Practice Notes in the Appendix refer to the 1963 Edition, and have been quoted from time to time to show the reader what has been the train of thought on contentious points.

A chapter on tendering procedure has been included as it is thought that nobody can successfully prepare a bill of variations and final accounts without a thorough understanding of this important precontract stage. A chapter has also been included which briefly describes with charts and text the structure of the building industry. This is by no means a fully comprehensive section, but I have tried to approach the topic from the viewpoint of the quantity surveyor. I have found from experience that very many young men are completely bewildered by the variety of organizations which the more experienced sections of the industry glibly refer to by means of mnemonic initials.

A brief section in this chapter sets out the structure and organization of a north-country firm known to me, in the hope that this will be helpful to many young men in professional offices and Local Authorities who have very little opportunity to get to know how a building firm works. This chapter should also be very useful for students taking examinations in Professional Practice and Procedure.

Finally I would like to make it clear that the methods I show in this book are not put forward as the only correct ways of dealing with the problems. I have tried to show the method which I consider to be the best chosen from many, but the reader must make his own final conclusion.

W.H.W. & A.A.B.W.

# 1. Variations

**Variations contemplated**

In most forms of contract used today for building work provision must be made for possible variations. At the time when tenders are invited the employer and his architect should have crystallized all their ideas into a set of contract documents, which usually consist of:

(a) a form of agreement
(b) a schedule of conditions
(c) a set of drawings
(d) a bill of quantities or a specification.

However, modern building is such a complex operation that it is essential that there should be a condition in the contract which will allow any necessary changes to be made. This condition is usually known as the 'variation clause'. Without it the contractor would have to agree to erect the building shown on the drawings and represented in the contract bills for the contract sum, and any minor change that the employer or his architect wished to make later would mean that the contract had to be cancelled and a new one drawn up. This would be very inconvenient, and could lay the employer open to a charge of breach of contract every time a change was made.

One of the disadvantages of the variation clause is that architects tend not always to crystallize their intentions on paper before the contract is signed. They do this because they know that the variation clause will permit them to finalize their intentions during the term of contract. These decisions should, however, always be made before tenders are invited; the variation clause should be used as little as possible, and then only for any unforeseen matters that may arise.

There are two standard forms of contract for building work: the JCT Standard Form of Building Contract issued by the Joint Contracts Tribunal and published by the RIBA, and the GC/Works/1 (2nd ed.) Form of Contract. The first is used for virtually all private building work in this country, and a specially adapted version of it is used in practically all Local Authority building. The second is the form of contract used by all Central Government departments for building and civil engineering work. (The initials 'GC' stand for 'Government Contracts'.)

Basically, the documents are very similar; there are only a few minor differences. In both forms of contract the architect or the superintending officer has power to issue instructions – referred to as 'architects' instructions' in the JCT form, and as 'superintending officer's instructions' in the GC/Works/1 form. These instructions can be issued to cover a wide variety of points, and it will be seen that although many of the instructions could constitute a variation, it does not follow that every instruction is a variation. Instructions must be confined to the following points:

### JCT forms (1963 Edition)
(a) Any discrepancy in or divergence between the Contact Drawings and/or the Contract Bills. See Clause 1 (2)
(b) Variations from the Contract Drawings or Contract Bills due to compliance with statutory obligations. See Clause 4 (1)
(c) The opening up for inspection of any work covered up or to arrange to carry out any test on any materials or goods. See Clause 6 (3)
(d) The removal from the site of any work materials or goods executed or brought thereon by the Contractor for the purposes of the Works. See Clause 11 (2)
(e) The removal from the site of any work materials or goods which are not in accordance with the Contract. See Clause 6 (4)
(f) The dismissal from the Works of any person employed thereon. See Clause 6 (5)
(g) The sanction in writing of any variation made by the Contractor otherwise than pursuant to an instruction of the Architect. See Clause 11 (1)
(h) The alteration or modification of the design quality or quantity of the Works as shown on the Contract Drawings and described by or referred to in the Contract Bills. See Clause 11 (2)
(i) The addition omission or substitution of any work. See Clause 11 (2)
(j) The alteration of the kind or standard of any material or goods to be used in the Works. See Clause 11 (2)
(k) The expenditure of prime cost and provisional sums included in the Contract Bills and of prime cost sums which arise as a result of instructions issued in regard to the expenditure of provisional sums. See Clause 11 (3)
(l) The making good of any defect shrinkage or other fault which shall appear within the Defects Liability Period which is due to materials or workmanship not in accordance with the Contract or frost occurring before the Practical Completion of the Works. See Clause 15 (3)
(m) The postponement of any work to be executed under the provisions of the Contract. See Clause 21 (2).

*GC/Works/1 form*

(a)  The variation or modification of the design quality or quantity of the Works or the addition or omission or substitution of any work
(b)  Any discrepancy in or between Specification and/or Bills of Quantities and/or Drawings
(c)  The removal from the site of any things for incorporation which are brought thereon by the Contractor and the substitution therefor of any other such things
(d)  The removal and/or re-execution of any work executed by the Contractor
(e)  The order of execution of the Works or any part thereof
(f)  The hours of working and the extent of overtime or nightwork to be adopted
(g)  The suspension of the execution of the Works or any part thereof
(h)  The replacement of any foreman or person below that grade employed in connection with the Contract
(i)  The opening up for inspection of any work covered up
(j)  The amending and making good of any defects under Condition 32
(k)  The execution in an emergency of work necessary for security
(l)  The use of materials obtained from excavations on the Site
(m)  Any other matter as to which it is necesary or expedient for the Superintending Officer to give instructions, directions, or explanations.

## Written instructions

Both forms of contract state that instructions must be given in writing or be subsequently confirmed in writing. From this it is quite clear that the quantity surveyor has no power to value variation instructions which are not given in the manner prescribed in the contract.

It is not essential for the variation instruction to be written on a special form headed 'variation order' or 'deviation order', but many architects, to avoid confusion, have special paper printed with the words 'Architect's Instruction' or 'Superintending Officer's Instruction' or 'Variation Order' as a heading, numbered in sequence, with provision for the architect's signature at the bottom. However, a variation in the form of a letter signed by the architect is just as valid. A drawing which shows extra work does not constitute a variation instruction even if it bears the architect's printed name – to be effective it must be signed by the architect (Myers *v*. Sarl 1860). However, an unsigned drawing dispatched with a covering letter signed by the architect which refers clearly to the particular drawing would be a valid instruction. It should be remembered that not all architects' instructions constitute a variation – for example, an instruction to remove defective work.

## Verbal instructions

Both forms of contract make provision for the conversion of verbal instructions into written instructions. GC/Works/1 states that oral instructions given by the superintending officer must be confirmed by him in writing, and that the contractor has the right to request written confirmation within fourteen days of such instructions being given.

The JCT form is not quite so dictatorial in this respect, and states that in the event of verbal instructions involving a variation being given to the contractor, such instructions shall be confirmed in writing by the contractor to the architect within seven days. If the architect does not write to the contractor to dissent from the written confirmation within a further seven days, then the written confirmation is deemed to be an architect's instruction.

The JCT form states in Clause 2 (3) that an oral instruction is not to have an immediate effect but must be confirmed in writing. When the architect confirms it in writing the instruction becomes effective immediately, but if the contractor has to write and confirm, it comes into operation only after the period stipulated in the clause.

If neither the architect nor the contractor confirms the oral instruction, but the contractor complies with it, the architect has the authority to confirm it in writing at any time before the final certificate is issued (see Clause 2 (3) (b)).

A further provision states that when he receives what purports to be an instruction issued by the architect the contractor may request the architect to specify in writing the contract condition which empowers him to issue it (see Clause 2 (2)).

## The agent

Clause 8 of the JCT form states that the contractor must keep upon the site a competent general foreman, and that any instructions given to him by the architect shall be deemed to be given to the contractor. This clause obviously refers to verbal instructions given to the foreman, and means that he may assume the powers of agency; he is therefore generally called the site agent nowadays. It should be noted that Condition 33 of the GC/Works/1 form uses the term 'agent'.

## The clerk of works

The JCT form clarifies the position of the clerk of works by deleting all reference to him from Clause 2 (Architect's Instructions). Clause 10 (Clerk of Works) states that any directions given to the contractor or his foreman by the clerk of works have no effect unless they refer to a matter for which the architect is empowered by the contract to issue instructions. Furthermore, to be effective, clerks of works' instructions have to be confirmed in writing by the architect within two working days of their being given.

The clerk of works is generally appointed by the employer, and owes his contractual duty to the employer through the architect. Nevertheless, the architect cannot use this for a defence should the employer sue him for negligence. The architect is not entitled to place implicit trust in the clerk of works, and though he may, apparently, delegate to the clerk of works the day-to-day supervision of the works, he still is himself responsible for major decisions.

These remarks do not apply to Central and Local Government contracts, where the superintending officer, the city architect, or the county architect have sole responsibility. All clerks of works, assistant architects, and quantity surveyors who are salaried employees are the chief officer's duly appointed representatives, and are responsible to the chief officer, who in turn assumes full responsibility for their decisions.

## Extent of variations

Clause 11 (1) of the JCT form ends with the following words: 'No variation required by the Architect or subsequently sanctioned by him in writing shall vitiate this contract', and Condition 7 (4) of the GC/Works/1 form states that 'such alterations additions or omissions shall not invalidate the contract'. It would appear from this that the architect has powers to vary the contract work as far as to instruct the contractor to carry out extra works not contemplated by the parties at the time the contract was signed. This, however, is not entirely true. For example, on a contract for building school buildings only, a variation may be issued instructing the contractor to construct all the playing fields. This instruction would nevertheless not constitute a valid variation to the contract.

In the agreement the contractor will have promised to do certain work that has been given in the contract bills of quantities, or shown on the contract drawings and described in the specification, with the condition that he will carry out any extra work that may be required. He has not agreed to carry out work which has no connection with the contract, but of course could always agree to do so if it were made the subject of a further contract. It should be clearly understood that the architect's powers to order extras applies only to 'things not specified in, nor fairly comprised within the contract, but cognate to the subject matter and applied to the carrying out of the design' (Russell *v.* Sada Banderia 1862).

## Variations of omission

Variations of omission may be ordered both by the architect under the JCT form and by the superintending officer under the GC/Works/1 form. Clause 11 (4) (d) of the JCT form, which deals with the valuation of variations, states that the rates contained in the contract bills will be used to value the items omitted. This is provided that if the omission substantially varies the conditions under which the remaining items are carried out, then the prices for such remaining work shall be valued at new rates, with the rates contained in the contract bills being used as a basis.

The power to order variations of omission is limited. If the omission is so extensive that it fundamentally alters the contract, then the employer might lay himself open to a claim of damages for breach of contract. Otherwise a contract may be signed, for example, for the erection of a house and garage, and an instruction issued omitting the house completely. Clause 11 (6) of the JCT form states that if the contractor suffers any direct loss and/or expense as a result of a variation valued according to this clause, then the architect or quantity surveyor must ascertain the amount, and add it to the contract sum. A claim for 'loss of anticipated profit' could come under this heading.

### Variations of omission: work given to another

The power to order variations applies only to work omitted in entirety, and not to work which the employer wishes to omit from the contract so that it can be carried out by another contractor. If the employer repudiates a binding contract by taking away part of the work and making this the subject of a contract with another, he lays himself open to an action for breach of contract (Gallagher v. Hirsch 1899).

This also applies to the omission of prime cost and provisional sums. They can be omitted entirely, but if they then become the subject of a separate contract a claim can be made for breach of contract and for any loss of profit on these items included in the contract sum. This would also be the case if the employer were to omit work and carry it out himself or with his own staff. For example, the provisional sum of £3000.00 may be included in a contract for the heating installation. The architect cannot subsequently omit this sum and inform the contractor that the employer intends to carry out the work with his own engineering staff.

In contracts based upon the GC/works/1 form of contract, under Condition 38 the employing authority reserves the right to order and pay direct for any item or portion of an item covered in the contract documents by a prime cost sum. However, under Condition 38 they do agree to pay the contractor's included profit on such items, *pro rata* to the amount paid direct by the employing authority.

# 2. Preparation of the variation account

## The surveyor's authority

### JCT form

In contracts based upon the JCT form the quantity surveyor is appointed in the Articles of Agreement, which are signed by the employer and the contractor. He is therefore equally responsible to both parties. The contractor can object to the appointment of the quantity surveyor at the time when the contract is signed or to his successor in the event of his death.

Before 1935 it was common practice for the quantity surveyor's fee to be included in the tender on the final summary. This fee was paid by the contractor out of his first payment on the contract: the 1957 Edition of the JCT form of contract still made an alternative provision for the payment to be made in this way, but in the current Edition this has been deleted. Today the quantity surveyor is usually paid his fee direct by the employer, although this does not affect his responsibility to the contractor. It has become common practice for the contractor to employ his own surveyor to measure with the quantity surveyor, but this does not alter the position, since the quantity surveyor measures 'with' the contractor's surveyor and not 'against' him.

The quantity surveyor's duties under the contract are limited to measuring and valuing the variations, and preparing the final account. He has only the authority to measure and value variations authorized by the architect in writing (Clause 11 (4)): clearly, therefore, it is not his responsibility to decide what is a variation and what is not.

The surveyor usually prepares the valuation of work done so that the architect can issue a certificate (Clause 30 (1)), but this is not specifically laid down in the contract. The architect alone has the authority to issue a certificate and he decides if a valuation should be made to arrive at the amount of the certificate. In practice, architects usually rely upon the quantity surveyor to prepare the valuations for interim certificates.

### GC/Works/1 form

The quantity surveyor is the person so designated in the Abstract of Particulars based on the GC/Works/1 form, but could be a salaried employee of the Government department contracting; he is therefore not acting in a strictly arbitrary capacity, as are the architect and surveyor in the JCT form, but solely in the interests of the employer. A quantity surveyor in private practice who is employed by the Government department contracting holds a different position from one employed under the JCT form of contract. In actual practice most Government surveyors and appointed quantity surveyors do act in the same arbitrary capacity when settling contracts, as under the JCT form. The strict interpretation of their position, however, is that they represent the employer alone.

The surveyor visits the works from time to time to take any notes and measurements required for the preparation of the final account. The quantity surveyor should give reasonable notice of the intended visit to the contractor, who can have a representative present to take the measurements together with the surveyor (Condition 37).

The preparation of the final account is the responsibility of the quantity surveyor, and should be presented in the manner prescribed by him (Conditions 41 (2) and 37 (2). If the contractor's representative fails to attend when required, the quantity surveyor has the power under the contract to measure and prepare the final account by himself (Condition 37 (1)).

The preparation of valuations for interim certificates under this form of contract differs from the procedure under the JCT form in that it is the contractor who prepares and submits a claim for payment, which is supported by a valuation. When the valuation has been agreed by the superintending officer he issues a certificate (Condition 40 (3)).

### Measurement and recording of variations

*Documents*
The surveyor should keep a special file for variations, which should be kept with all the other documents referring to the contract. Copies of the instructions issued by the architect should be filed here in numerical order. It is good practice for architects to forward copies of architect's instructions (AIs) to the quantity surveyor and the clerk of works, since the originals always remain in the possession of the contractor.

All correspondence relating to variations should be kept in this file. If it is important not to interfere with the date sequence of the main correspondence files, photo copies should be made and inserted instead. All copies of drawings received which relate to variations should be clearly marked in red as variation drawings, and be kept in the variation file. A file which provides some method of clipping letters together, and a large pocket to hold drawings, is best for the purpose.

*Site visits*
The frequency of site visits will depend upon the size of the contract and the number of variations. On a small contract the main visits can be confined to those made each month for the preparation of interim certificates. After the

valuation has been prepared any variations can be measured on site if necessary. On a larger contract site meetings will probably be arranged at regular intervals of a week or a fortnight; these will be attended by the architect, consultants, clerk of works, the contractor's agent, surveyors, and sub-contractors. Although many points will be discussed that do not affect the quantity surveyor, it is still advisable for him to attend, so that he can get a clear picture of progress. After the meeting finishes there is a very good opportunity to measure variations, since the contractor's surveyor will be present.

It should be noted that the surveyor must inform the contractor when he intends to visit the site to measure variations, so that the contractor's surveyor can be present (JCT Clause 11 (4)) (GC/Works/1 Condition 37 (1)). As has been said, the surveyor has only the authority to measure variations actually confirmed in writing. Although the contractor is responsible for applying for AIs, the surveyor should watch for any variations that may be taking place, particularly variations of omission, so that he can advise the architect that an AI should be issued.

When the surveyor and the contractor's surveyor agree that an AI will be necessary or when the contractor's surveyor states that he intends to ask for an AI the work concerned should be recorded at the time, particularly if the work is to be subsequently covered up. This practice ensures that should an AI be issued, there can be no dispute as to the extent and nature of the work done. If an AI is not issued no harm has been done, and the fact that measurements have been recorded simply for 'record purposes' does not commit either party. It is important that the value of such work should not be included in any payment until the AI has been issued.

### Measuring

Each AI should be taken in turn and the necessary measurements recorded. The method is to omit the work contained in the contract bills from details in the original dimensions, and to add the measurements for the work as carried out. Some surveyors make only net adjustments, but this is bad practice. If an AI is issued which increases the width of a door from 626 to 726 mm it is very unsatisfactory to attempt to measure 100 mm extra of paint, frame, architrave, flooring, lintel, and so on, and to deduct 100 mm of plaster, decoration, and skirting and moreover this does not reflect the nature of the variation.

The dimensions for each variation should be started on a new sheet of dimension paper or a new page of the dimension book. There should be a clear heading giving the AI number, date issued, date measured, and a brief description of the variation for identification purposes.

In the simpler form of variation only a single item or group of items in the contract bills is varied. After a brief check with the original dimensions the item or group of items can be omitted in entirety by a clear reference to the page number of the contract bills and to the item numbers. The varied work can then be measured and recorded as additions, as shown in Example A. If the variation is more complex the omission will be recorded and reference made to the original dimensions, giving the column numbers and stating very clearly where the omission begins and ends. If the variation is very complicated it is better to copy the omissions, item by item, from the original dimensions, as shown in Example B. Although the omissions are always taken directly from the contract bills or from the original dimensions, the additions often have to be measured on site if a drawing of the variation has not been issued. When a drawing is available, however, it should be used for measurements, preferably in the site office, where any difficulty can be resolved immediately by checking with the actual work.

**Example A: The Recording of Variations**

| | | | | | | | |
|---|---|---|---|---|---|---|---|
| | *AI No.: 42* | | *Issued: 25/9/79* | | | | |
| | *Measured: 1/10/79* | | | | | | |
| | *Description* | | | | | | |
| | Omit oak architraves to all internal doors, and substitute softwood | | | | | | |
| | *Omit* | | | | | | |
| | Page 43, item G-J inclusive | | | | | | |
| | *Add* | | | | | | |
| 25/ 2/ 2/ | 2.30 | 230.00 | 75 × 25 mm softwood moulded architrave, planted on hardwood frame, including mitres and ends | | | | |
| 25/ 2/ | 1.00 | 50.00 | | | | | |
| | | 280.00 | | | | | |
| 5/ 2/ 2/ | 2.75 | 55.00 | 100 × 25 mm ditto | | | | |
| 5/ 2/ | 1.25 | 12.50 | | | | | |
| | | 67.50 | | | | | |

It is extremely important in recording dimensions that omissions should be kept distinct from additions. Some surveyors therefore prefer to enter all omissions in red ink and additions in black ink. Every column in the dimensions should be headed with the words OMIT or ADD in capital letters underlined, since if the worker-up were to confuse this in any way it could have serious consequences.

*Example B: The Recording of Variations*

AI No.:42     Issued: 25/11/79

Measured: 1/12/79

Description

Omit oak architraves to doors 22, 23, 24, and substitute softwood

| *Omit* | | | | *Add* | | |
|---|---|---|---|---|---|---|
| Original dimensions, columns 249–250 inclusive, as below | | | | *Doors 22 and 23* | | |
| | | | | 2/ | | | 75 × 25 mm softwood moulded archi- |
| | | | | 2/ | 2.30 | 9.20 |
| | | | | 2/ | 1.00 | 2.00 | trave, planted on hardwood frame |
| *Doors 22 & 23* | | | | | | 11.20 | including mitres |
| 2/ | | 75 × 25 mm oak | | | | | and ends |
| 2/ | 2.30 | 9.20 | architrave as | | | | |
| 2/ | 1.00 | 2.00 | described | | | | |
| | | 11.20 | | | | | |
| | | | | *Door 24* | | |
| | | | | 2/ | 2.75 | 5.50 | 100 × 25 mm |
| | | | | | 1.25 | 1.25 | ditto |
| *Door 24* | | | | | | 6.75 |
| 2/ | 2.75 | 5.50 | 100 × 25 mm | | | |
| | 1.25 | 1.25 | oak architrave | | | |
| | | 6.75 | as described | | | |
| 2 | | Mits | | | | |

*Example C: The Recording of Variations*

Contract No.: ...................

House No.: ...................

Type: ...................

Floor Level: ...................

*For Calculation Purposes*

T =
C =

T =
C =

T =
C =

Average Int. Walls

T =
C =

Average Int. Walls

T =
C =

Average Int. Walls

T =
C =

T =
C =

T =
C =

T =
C =

T =
C =

T =
C =

T =
C =

Kerb Level

□ = Existing ground level
T = Depth of trench dig
C = Depth of concrete wall

150 mm soil strip   Yes/No
Fill = Earth ash hardcore
Dig = Normal % soft rock
         % hard rock

⌐| = Mark step and depth in wall

Site Measurements By

Corporation

Date:

Contractor:

Sometimes a variation applies to a section of the work that will be immediately covered up, such as drainage. If it is not possible for the surveyor to be present at the time that the work is done arrangements should be made with the clerk of works and the contractor's foreman or agent to record the necessary information; this may then be presented to the quantity surveyor and the contractor's surveyor, who measure the variation. It is necessary to leave detailed instructions about the information required with the clerk of works before the work begins, since very few clerks of works understand how the dimensions will be entered. The quantity surveyor must satisfy himself as to the accuracy of any dimensions taken on his behalf by the clerk of works or anyone else, as the quantity surveyor is responsible for the final account and the measurements and prices therein.

On large housing contracts many Local Authorities issue charts of foundation details, which the clerk of works and the contractor's foreman complete. If these charts are carefully designed, and are signed by the clerk of works and foreman, the quantity surveyor can use them to measure variations, instead of having to travel each time to the site. Example C shows this type of chart.

## Working up the measurements

The surveyor should not attempt to square out the dimensions as he records the variations, but should leave this until later. Very often a small variation can be billed direct from the dimensions, but when the variation is complicated it may be necessary to draw up a special abstract. The abstract should be arranged in trade order, but omissions and additions should be recorded on separate abstract sheets, preferably with the omissions written in red ink and the additions in black. It is very important to abstract omissions and additions on separate sheets, since otherwise confusion can arise with the abstracting of deductions.

There is an alternative method of recording variations which can be used to solve the difficulty of working up. A special ruled paper or dimension book is used, on which dimensions, descriptions, rates, and cash extensions can be written. A typical sheet of this type of paper is shown in Example D. By this system a single document can be produced which contains all the information required in the bill of variations. No abstracting and billing is required if the variations are carefully recorded on the sheets, so that the items are priced, extended, and cast in the order in which they are measured. From these sheets a summary of variations can be typed which will give all the information normally required by the employer and the architect. It is advisable for the contractor's surveyor to record dimensions on a similar piece of paper.

In Example D it will be seen that only a single cash column has been used. Omissions and additions should therefore be entered on separate sheets, and this should be clearly indicated at the top of the sheet with the word 'Omissions' or 'Additions' in block capitals. A different method of entering

*Example D: The Billing of Variations*

| | | | | | | | | Additions | |
|---|---|---|---|---|---|---|---|---|---|
| | AI No. 22 | | | | | | | £ | p |
| | *Issued: 14/7/79* | | | | | | | | |
| | *Measured: 19/8/79* | | | | | | | | |
| | *Description* | | | | | | | | |
| | 50 mm precast concrete paving slabs in area to the rear of the oil store | | | | | | | | |
| | *Additions* | | | | | | | | |
| | 9.00 | | Exc. o/s. av. 200 mm deep to remove veg. soil | *PR.* 22/A | | | | | |
| | 3.00 | 27.00 | | 22/B | 32 sq. m | 60p | | 19 | 20 |
| ½/ | 9.00 | | & | | | | | | |
| | 1.00 | 4.50 | load topsoil, wheel 100 metres and deposit cube × 0.20 | | | | | | |
| | | 31.50 | | 22/R | 6 cub. m | 1.50 | | 9 | 00 |
| | | | & | | | | | | |
| | | | 75 mm bed of broken stone hardcore | 23/G | 32 sq. m | 75p | | 24 | 00 |
| | | | & | | | | | | |
| | | | 50 mm thick precast vibrated concrete paving slabs, as described | 41/K | 32 sq. m | 3.00 | | 96 | 00 |
| | 10.00 | | R.c. to last | * | 10 m | 75p | | 7 | 50 |
| | 2 | | Cut & fit slabs around gulley | 41/L | 2 No | 85p | | 1 | 70 |
| | | | *AI. No. 22* *to Summary* | | *Additions* | | £ | 157 | 40 |

item reference numbers is also shown in Example D: here numbers are entered in a special reference column, not after the descriptions in brackets as previously suggested. When a completely new item occurs in the variation account, and has been agreed by means of a 'fair valuation', it is good practice to indicate it with a star, as with the item for raking cutting in Example D.

## Billing of variations

Variations are billed from the abstract sheets, or, as already mentioned, direct from the dimension sheets. The surveyor should guide the worker-up in the arrangement of the variation account. It helps the client if variations are presented in groups, if this is possible, rather than as dozens of individual variations in numerical order, each having a cash value. The surveyor, however, must use his discretion in this matter and judge every case on its merits.

*Example E: The Billing of Variations*

| | | | Omissions £ | Omissions p | | Additions £ | Additions p |
|---|---|---|---|---|---|---|---|
| AI: No. 42 | | | | | | | |
| Issued: 25/12/79 | | | | | | | |
| Measured: 1/1/80 | | | | | | | |
| Description Omit the oak architraves to doors 22, 23, 24, and substitute softwood | | | | | | | |
| Omissions 75 × 25 mm oak architraves as described. (43/G) | 11 m | 2.05 | 22 | 55 | | | |
| 100 × 25 mm ditto (43/I) | 7 m | 3.30 | 23 | 10 | | | |
| Mitres (43/J) | 2 No. | 30p | | 60 | | | |
| Additions 75 × 25 mm softwood architrave moulded, planted on hardwood frame, including all labours (PR. 86/B) | 11 m | | | | 1.40 | 15 | 40 |
| 100 × 25 mm ditto (PR.86/B) | 7 m | | | | 1.95 | 13 | 65 |
| Totals to Summary | | | £ 46 | 25 | | £ 29 | 05 |

Some surveyors prefer to deduct one total from another, and transfer a net omission or addition to the variation account summary. The best method is to carry both totals to the final summary, so that more information is given in the document. The net difference can be worked out mentally, but a net omission of £0.25 against a variation of some magnitude on a final summary will, of course, appear ridiculous, especially to the layman. A specimen page from a bill of variations is shown in Example E.

The omissions need not be written with full descriptions in the bill of variations, as they should in the contract bills. The description should be written briefly, and the page and item reference number should be entered after it in brackets or placed in an appropriate column. When a group of items is omitted entirely from the contract bills it is not necessary to write down each item; a brief reference for the page and item numbers can be written in the description column and a lump-sum cash total entered in the omissions column. This should be done with care, since the cash amount may not be checked again.

### Time for preparation of the bill of variations

#### JCT form
Under Clause 30 (5) (a) of this form of contract it is the duty of the surveyor to prepare a priced bill of variations not later than the end of 'the period of final measurement' which is stated in the appropriate place in the appendix to the conditions of contract. This period will usually be stated in months and is agreed by the parties before the contract is signed. It comes into operation upon the practical completion of the contract.

The clause states that if the parties fail to complete this part of the appendix the period of final measurement automatically becomes six months from the practical completion of the contract. The term 'practical completion' often causes confusion, but it is generally held to be the date when the building is handed over as ready for occupation. The 'defects liability period' also usually starts at this date. Clause 15 (1) of the JCT form makes provision for the architect to issue a 'certificate of practical completion'.

#### GC/Works/1 form
As has already been said, it is the duty of the quantity surveyor under the GC/Works/1 form of contract to supply a final account. This account is to be delivered as soon as possible after the completion of the works, and there is therefore no fixed time limit (Condition 41 (2)).

#### Time for pricing variations
To obtain the maximum benefit from the measured and agreed variations it is good practice to agree rates with the contractor at the earliest opportunity. It is advisable to do this at the time the measurements are recorded if possible.

Early pricing has the advantage that the variations can be brought into certificate valuations from the time that they are measured. Also, the quantity surveyor can render an excellent service to the architect by keeping him informed of the cost of variations as the work progresses; this allows him to see at a glance the financial position of the contract. Sometimes contractors are a little wary of early agreement, but this system has many advantages from their point of view also. Clause 11 (5) of the JCT form lays down that measured and valued variations shall be included in interim certificates.

### Complete remeasurement

If a contract has not been well planned, or has been let in a hurry, the variations may be so extensive that it is simpler to remeasure whole sections of the work, or in extreme cases even to remeasure the whole of the works. The surveyor has no authority to take this decision himself, but must first obtain the agreement of both parties to the contract. This is because the contract is based upon omissions and additions and does not allow for complete remeasurement. The client could be faced in this case with a re-measurement fee from the surveyor, and perhaps a claim from the contractor for the cost of the attendance of his representative during the remeasurement.

A complete section of the work, however, such as the foundations, can be remeasured if the architect will issue an AI. This complies with the procedure laid down in the contract.

### Provisional quantities

Sometimes the ultimate extent of a certain section of the work will not be known when the bill of quantities is being prepared; for example, when a builder is working in attendance upon specialist engineers. To cover this possibility, quantity surveyors often include in the contract bills a section containing a representative set of items. These quantities are clearly headed in the bills as PROVISIONAL.

The surveyor must adjust these items in the final account by omitting the entire section and replacing it with the actual work as measured on site. Occasionally the provisional quantities in fact represent the actual work done, but the same procedure must still be followed since this shows that the measurement has not been overlooked. No AI is required as authority for the adjustment of provisional quantities. The fact that they were marked as provisional in the contract bills shows that the parties to the contract contemplated remeasurement. However, on contracts based upon the GC/Works/1 form of contract, a written order is required under Condition 39 before work covered by provisional quantities can begin.

### Errors in bills of quantities

Errors in contract bills are dealt with in Clause 12 of the JCT form of contract and in Condition 5 of the GC/Works/1 form. Sometimes, however, these clauses are misunderstood. This is because contractors occasionally think that the clauses provide for the rectification of errors which have arisen in the unit rates or cash extensions and totals. This view is wrong, since it is only errors in the information supplied to contractors in contract bills – that is, errors in the descriptions and/or quantity columns – that can be corrected in this way. Form GC/Works/1 makes this quite clear by stating that this condition does not cover the rectification of errors or omission of prices or computations in the bills of quantities. If any error should arise in the quantity or description of an item, or its complete omission, it should be treated as a variation and dealt with under the procedure laid down in Clause 11 of the JCT form, or Condition 9 of the GC/Works/1 form. The JCT form clarifies the position about arithmetical errors. In Clause 13 it lays down that errors in the computations of the contract sum in the signed contract bills are deemed to have been accepted by both parties. It is the duty of the contractor to inform the architect in writing of any error that he discovers in the contract bills (Clause 1 (2) – JCT form). Both parties have the right to ask for the remeasurement of any item or section of the contract bills, provided that this right is reasonably exercised.

The JCT form states that the contract bills should be prepared in accordance with the principles of the Standard Method of Measurement of Building Work. Many surveyors, however, make an overriding provision in the preliminaries section of their bills of quantities that although the quantities are prepared in accordance with the principles of the Standard Method of Measurement, nevertheless the method of measurement used in the bills of quantities will prevail. This is possible because the Standard Method of Measurement is a definition of principle aimed at providing a uniform method of measurement rather than an inflexible document.

In exceptional cases surveyors can use their own discretion and adopt special methods, so long as they follow the agreed principles of measurement and make their intention clear to the contractor when tendering. If when preparing his bills of quantities a surveyor expressly stated that the cost of earthwork support must be included in the excavation items, the contractor could not win a legal claim for this to be paid for as an error in the bills of quantities. If, however, earthwork support had not been measured or expressly mentioned in the bills of quantities then the claim would succeed, since this would be an error of omission. Under the JCT form a general overriding clause in the contract bills is no longer sufficient: the contractor's attention must be specifically drawn to every single departure from the Standard Method of Measurement. See Clause 12 (1) and note the words 'expressly stated'.

Disputes about errors of quantity or omission are often easily resolved, since they are a matter of fact. Those involving errors in description, however, are often very complicated. The contractor and the surveyor dispute the meaning of the terms and usually they end by going to arbitration. The simpler type of error of description occurs where the description of an item differs from the description on the drawing and the architect requires the work to be executed as shown on the drawing. This would be rectified as an error of description (see Clause 12 (2) JCT form or Condition 5 (2) of the GC/Works/1 form).

# 3. Valuation of variations

## Contracts with quantities

### JCT form

Clause 11 of this form of contract sets out the methods that are to be used for the valuation of variations; these are briefly stated below.

(1) Where work is measured which is of a similar character, and executed under similar conditions to an item in the contract bills, then the unit price of such an item shall be used.

(2) Where varied work is measured which is not of a similar character, nor executed under similar conditions to an item in the contract bills, then where possible the unit price of such an item shall be used as a basis for the new price. The use of a bill item must not be extended to the stage where it becomes unreasonable to use this rate as a basis for pricing.

(3) When it is not practicable to apply a contract bills price, either direct or as a basis, then a fair valuation must be made and agreed by the parties

(4) When varied work cannot be properly measured and valued the contractor shall, unless otherwise agreed, be allowed:

    (a) The prime cost of such work calculated in accordance with the 'Definition of Prime Cost of Daywork carried out under a Building Contract' issued by the RICS and the NFBTE together with percentage additions to each section of the prime cost at the rates set out in the contract bills and recorded in the appendix to those Conditions; or

    (b) Where the work is within the province of any specialist trade and the said Institution and the body representing the employers in that trade have agreed and issued a definition of prime cost of daywork, the prime cost of such work calculated in accordance with that definition as issued together with percentage additions on the prime cost rates set out in the contract bills and recorded in the appendix to these Conditions.

(5) Variations of omission shall be priced at the rates in the contract bills, provided that if the omission substantially varies the conditions under which any remaining items of work are carried out, then the prices for

such remaining items shall be valued as set out in method No. 2. Note, however, that Clause 11 (6) states that if the architect thinks a variation has involved the contractor in direct loss or expense for which he would not be repaid under Clause 11 (4) (for example, a variation involving the re-erection of scaffolding), then the architect or quantity surveyor is to ascertain the amount, and it is to be added to the contract sum.

### GC/Works/form

Condition 9 (1) of this form of contract is very similar to that in the JCT form, and states that the following methods shall be used for the valuation of variations:

(1) Varied work shall be valued in accordance with the rates and prices contained in the bills of quantities for similar work, in so far as such prices shall apply

(2) When the net prices contained in the bills of quantities do not apply, then the value shall be based upon, or be deduced from, the items in the bills of quantities, in so far as it is practicable to do so

(3) When it is not practicable to apply a bills of quantities price for varied work, or deduce a price therefrom, then rates and prices shall be agreed on a fair valuation basis

(4) When varied work cannot properly be valued by measurement and valuation, then daywork rates included in the contract shall be used.

In the JCT form provision is made for the revaluation of remaining work, when variations of omission are extensive (Clause 11 (4) (d)). This is not done in the GC/works/1 form. Although the condition is not specifically stated, however, it could be argued that if there are extensive omissions, it is not practicable to apply the bills of quantities prices to the remaining work. If the balance of a contract is materially upset because of extensive variations it is reasonable to expect that a claim for the substitution of negotiated rates would be successful, provided that such rates made recompense for the disturbance (Condition 9 (2) (a)).

## Contracts without quantities

### JCT form

The following are the contract documents for a contract without quantities:

(1) form of agreement and schedule of conditions
(2) drawings
(3) specification
(4) schedule of rates.

When no bills of quantities are supplied the contractor has to prepare his own quantities from the drawings and specification. In this type of contract the specification has to contain far more information, and is consequently brought into the contract.

In contracts with quantities the specification is not a contract document, but only indicates where the various items are situated in the building. The bills of quantities should contain everything in the specification that affects cost, and, together with the contractor's prices, acts as a schedule of rates for the valuation of variations. This is why the specification is not a contract document, since it serves only to assist the actual constructors on the site, such as the site agent and the clerk of works.

A schedule of rates is prepared to deal with the difficulties which can arise over the valuing of variations where there are no bills of quantities. This contains some of the major items that are likely to be affected by variations. The contractor puts against the particular item in this document the unit rate he has used in the preparation of his tender; he knows that if these rates are agreed they will be used to value variations.

The schedule of rates is virtually a condensed bill of quantities without a quantity column. The rates inserted in this document should be studied very carefully before they are accepted and passed as reasonable, since the schedule could have a considerable effect upon the final account if there were extensive variations. Sometimes this schedule is drawn up by the architect, but very often the contractor is asked to submit a schedule before the contract is signed. For this reason architects are advised to employ a quantity surveyor to draw up the schedule and report on the inserted rates. The quantity surveyor has expert knowledge to decide if the rates are reasonable, and also which items are most likely to vary.

The five methods of valuation set out in the form used with quantities are used in this form also, with the words 'schedule of rates' substituted for 'contract bills'. From this it will be seen that any variation in items not contained in the schedule of rates will be priced by means of fair valuation or on a daywork basis.

### GC/Works/1

When contracts based upon this form are made without bills of quantities a schedule of rates or build-up of the tender is required. The form of contract is prepared for use with either bills of quantities or a schedule of rates, and in contracts without quantities the words 'schedule of rates' contained in the contract are automatically read. The same rules apply for pricing.

### Examples of valuations

#### *Example 1*

*Item in bills of quantity*
(1)  Concrete (21 MN/m²) in 300 ×
       100 mm precast coping, weathered, twice
       throated and bedded in cement mortar. 1.3   RATE = £3.80 per m

*Item in variation account*
(1) Concrete (21 MN/m²) in 250 ×
    100 mm precast coping, weathered, twice throated
    and bedded in cement mortar 1.3 . .    . . PRO-RATA RATE = £3.17 per m

*Calculations*

300 × 100 mm coping = £3.80 per m
250 × 100 mm coping =

$$\frac{250 \times 100}{300 \times 100} = \frac{5}{6} \times \frac{£3.80}{1} = £3.17$$

## Example 2

*Items in bills of quantity*
(2) Concrete (21 MN/m²) in 150 ×
    150 mm precast threshold, finished fair all
    round and bedded in cement mortar 1.3 ··   RATE = £2.70 per m
(3) Ditto in 200 × 150 mm ditto ··   ··   ··   RATE = £3.50 per m

*Calculations*
Additional area = 7,500 mm² Additional cost = £0.80

*Item in variation account*
Concrete (21 MN/m²) in 200 ×
200 mm precast threshold, finished fair all round
and bedded in cement mortar 1.3 . .    . .   PRO-RATA = £4.57 per m

*Calculations*
200 × 200 = 40,000 mm²
150 × 150 = 22,500 mm² = £2.70
           17,500 mm²

$$\frac{17,500}{7,500} \times \frac{£0.80}{1} = \frac{1.87}{£4.57}$$

In this example both items 2 and 3 must be used in the calculation.

## Contract bill items
(4) Excavate to form foundation trench not exceeding 2.00 m deep, commencing at
    ground level. RATE = £2.00 per cub. m.
(5) Ditto, not exceeding 4.00 m deep ditto. RATE = £2.50 per cub. m.
(6) Excavate to form basement not exceeding 2.00 m deep, commencing at ground
    level. RATE = £1.75 per cub. m.
(7) Load up surplus excavated material wheel 100 m, and deposit in spoil heaps.
    RATE = £1.50 per cub. m.
(8) Ditto, but wheel 150 m, and ditto. RATE = £1.70 per cub. m.
(9) Load up surplus excavated material, wheel 100m, deposit spread and level in
    150 mm layers. RATE = £2.00 per cub. m.

### Item in variation account

Excavate to form basement not exceeding 4.00 m deep,    Item 5    £2.50
commencing at ground level                „   4    £2.00

£0.50 additional
depth

It would be incorrect to add
£0.50 to the basement rate
of £1.75, since the nature of
the two types of excavation
is different. The extra depth
of basement excavation will
increase in proportion to the
surface trench excavation as
follows:

$$\frac{£1.75}{£2.00} \times £2.50 = £2.188$$

RATE = £2.188 cub. m   P.R. 4/5/6


### Item in variation account

Load up surplus excavated material, wheel 200 m,   Item    8 £1.70
deposit spread and level in 150 mm layers ..     „     7 £1.50

cost of 50 m additional wheeling £0.20
Therefore cost of 100 m additional wheeling = £0.40
Item 9 ..     ..   = £2.00

£2.40

RATE = £2.40 cube m
P.R. 7/8/9


Very often items occur where a straightforward *pro rata* is not possible. Nevertheless, the contract bills rate can be used as a basis for pricing, together with other small factors which have to be agreed. Here is an example of such a case:

### Bills of quantities item

(11) 100 mm diameter spun iron drainpipes to B.S.1211, laid in drain trench,
with flexible gland joints

| | | £ p |
|---|---|---|
| Invoice cost of pipes per metre | | 4.00 |
| Add Waste, say 10% | | 0.40 |
| | | 4.40 |
| Add Overheads and profit, say 10% | | 0.44 |
| | | 4.84 |
| Cost of 1 m of pipe at bill rate | | 8.39 |
| Deduct cost of 1 m of pipe plus waste and profit | | 4.84 |
| Cost of laying and jointing | | 3.55 |

### Item in variation account

100 mm diameter spun iron drainpipes
to B.S.1211, with glass lining, laid in trench
with flexible gland joints

| | £ p |
|---|---|
| Invoice cost of 1 m of glass lined pipe .. | 5.50 |
| Add Waste, say 10% | 0.55 |
| | 6.05 |
| Add Overheads and profit, say 10% .. | 0.605 |
| Add cost of laying and jointing .. .. | 3.55 |
| Cost of 1 m of pipe | £10.205 |

RATE = £10.205 per lin. m
P.R.11.

Care must be taken to make allowances, if necessary, for minor sundry
materials and also for additional labour costs in respect of extra handling or
fixing time.

# 4. Daywork accounts

**JCT form**

Clause 11 (4) (c) (i) of the JCT form states that if work cannot be properly measured and valued then the contractor shall (unless otherwise agreed) be allowed the prime cost of such work calculated in accordance with the 'Definition of Prime Cost of Daywork carried out under a Building Contract' last before issued by the RICS and NFBTE together with percentage additions to each section of the prime cost at the rates set out by the contractor in the contract bills (see Appendix D for a copy of this document).

The percentage additions can be set out on the form of tender for the contractor to insert or separate sums included in the bills of quantities for labour, materials and plant and the contractor is given the opportunity to insert the percentage addition necessary to cover all the items listed in the definition. The bills of quantities may be drawn up as follows:

Bill no. 12
Daywork
Provisional

| | £ | p | £ | p |
|---|---|---|---|---|
| Daywork will only be permitted when authorized in writing by the architect, and the same shall be paid for as laid down in Clause 11 (4) (c) (i) and (ii) | | | | |
| The Contractor shall add the percentage additions on prime cost he requires on the following and include the total so derived in the tender | | | | |
| *Builder's own work* The sum of £1,000.00 (one thousand pounds) for labour | 1000 | 00 | | |
| Add percentage addition | | | | |
| The sum of £500.00 (five hundred pounds) for materials | 500 | 00 | | |
| Add percentage addition | | | | |
| The sum of £300.00 (three hundred pounds) for plant | 300 | 00 | | |
| Add percentage addition | | | | |
| *Specialist trade work*–(specialist to be stated) The sum of £200.00 (two hundred pounds) for labour | 200 | 00 | | |
| Add percentage addition | | | | |
| The sum of £75.00 (seventy-five pounds) for materials | 75 | 00 | | |
| Add percentage addition | | | | |
| The sum of £75.00 (seventy-five pounds) for plant | 75 | 00 | | |
| Add percentage addition | | | | |
| *Carried to main Summary* | | £ | | |

Note: Daywork carried out during the Defects Liability Period would justify different percentages.

### GC/Works/1 form

Condition 9 (1) (d) of the GC/Works/1 form of contract states that where variations cannot be valued by measurement, or the value otherwise be agreed, then the work shall be valued at the daywork rates inserted in the contract.

In contracts based upon this form a page can be provided in the bills of quantities, or the schedule of rates, where the contractor can insert his rates, using either of the two previous methods. However, most employing authorities prefer to include a provisional sum for the net labour cost and a provisional sum for the net materials cost used in daywork; they instruct the contractor to insert his required percentage addition immediately after the item. This item is generally put in the preliminaries section, but not inevitably. One of the advantages of this method is that the contractor's percentage additions are reflected in the tender figure, and this does help to prevent inflated percentages from being added. Although GC/Works/1 form does not specifically refer to the 'Definition of Prime Cost of Daywork' issued by the RICS and NFBTE, it is usual to include this reference as a basis by suitable clauses in the specification documents.

Another method is used by some employing authorities, which also allows the contractor's daywork rates to be reflected in the tender figure. Here the contractor is asked to insert inclusive rates against a provisional number of hours for craftsmen and labourers. Materials are still dealt with by a percentage addition.

### Recording daywork on site

Both the JCT form and the GC/Works/1 form make provision for recording daywork on site. The contractor should complete a voucher specifying the actual work, the daily time spent (usually with the workmen's names entered), and the materials used. Many contractors have specially printed daywork sheets, with duplicate and triplicate copies, which are used to record daywork on the sites. This sheet should be signed by the clerk of works and the site agent, although this does not mean that the work will necessarily be finally valued on a daywork basis; this decision rests with the quantity surveyor. The signatures merely certify that the hours and materials recorded are correct. From the contractor's point of view it is good practice to record any doubtful variation on daywork sheets, even if the work is eventually measured, since the sheets can often assist the quantity surveyor in the agreement of a fair valuation.

### JCT form

Clause 11 (4) (c) sets out how daywork should be recorded. The contractor is to supply vouchers specifying the time spent daily on the daywork; if required by the architect the workmen's names must also be entered. In addition the materials used must be recorded. The vouchers must be delivered to the architect or his authorised representative not later than the end of the week after that in which the daywork has been executed.

## GC/Works/1 form

The recording of daywork is set out in Condition 24, which states that the contractor must give the superintending officer reasonable notice of the commencement of work ordered to be executed on a daywork basis. The contractor is to deliver to the superintending officer a return giving full detailed accounts of the labour and materials used on the dayworks. The

*Example F: Daywork Accounts*

| | | £ | p | £ | p |
|---|---|---|---|---|---|
| *AI No. 16*<br>*Issued: 30/9/79* | | | | | |
| *Executed: 1/10/79*  *Daywork sheet: 8* | | | | | |
| *Description:*<br>Demolish brick wall at East end of playground<br>and make good paved areas | | | | | |
| *Labour:* | | | | | |
| 16 hours labourer | 1.50 | 24 | 00 | | |
| 6 hours craftsman | 1.75 | 10 | 50 | | |
| 2 hours diesel roller driver | 1.60 | 3 | 20 | | |
| | | 37 | 70 | | |
| Percentage addition | 90% | 33 | 93 | | |
| | | | | 71 | 63 |
| *Materials:* | | | | | |
| 200 kg, 40 mm coarse tarmacadam | 10p | 20 | 00 | | |
| 500 kg, sand | 5p | 25 | 00 | | |
| 50 kg, 12 mm fine tarmacadam | 15p | 7 | 50 | | |
| | | 52 | 50 | | |
| Percentage addition | 10% | 5 | 25 | 57 | 75 |
| *Plant* | | | | | |
| 2 hours diesel roller (local hire rate) | 3.00 | 6 | 00 | | |
| Percentage addition | 10% | 0 | 60 | 6 | 60 |
| *Total to Summary* | | | £ | 135 | 98 |

return is to be submitted within one week of the end of the pay week in which the daywork was executed. If the returns are found to be correct a copy of each voucher will be certified by the superintending officer and returned to the contractor.

### Checking daywork accounts

When the surveyor receives the daywork sheets he should check them to see to which A I's they relate, and also make a note of the sheets that will be superseded by measurement and those covered by the work in the bills of quantities. The sheets should be checked for any inconsistencies, such as excessive or deficient quantities of materials, and the surveyor should note cases where the time recorded appears excessive, so that he is prepared for consultation with the contractor's representative.

A specimen daywork account is given in Example F. Some surveyors, however, prefer to total all the labour, materials, and plant expended in daywork, and thus to obtain one final total for each of these sections. They can then apply the percentage additions at the end. The only disadvantage of this system is that a true total cost for each operation is not visible in the account.

# 5. Prime cost and provisional sums

## Definitions

Prime cost and provisional sums are approximate sums of money which contractors are instructed to include in their tenders to cover the cost of the following:

(a) Work executed by specialist sub-contractors, nominated or selected by the architect; for example, specialist flooring contractors.
(b) Goods supplied by suppliers, nominated or selected by the architect, but fixed by the general contractor; for example, ironmongery
(c) Work executed by statutory undertakers; for example, gas, water, or electrical mains installations
(d) Sections of work usually executed by the general contractor during the course of the contract, the exact nature of which is not known at the time of tendering; for example, repairs to existing structure.

The advantage of this procedure is that the employer does not have to enter into a series of separate contracts. After the initial nomination these specialists become the sub-contractors and suppliers to the general contractor, who is then responsible for the co-ordination of the work and the ordering of materials.

The terms 'prime cost' (P.C.) and 'provisional sum' often causes confusion, since frequently either term is used in the bills of quantities in relation to nominated sub-contractors and nominated suppliers. It is possible to determine, however, which to use – that is, whether to use Clause 27 or Clause 28 of the JCT form of contract. Clause 27 applies where the sum is included for persons to be nominated both to supply and to fix materials and to execute work on site; Clause 28 applies where the sum is included in respect of materials or goods supplied only by a nominated supplier and fixed by the contractor.

Many surveyors have tried to distinguish between the terms in their bills of quantities by using 'provisional sum' for sums included for work to be executed by a specialist sub-contractor selected or nominated by the architect. The term 'prime cost' is then used for sums included for goods to be supplied by suppliers selected or nominated by the architect and to be fixed by the general contractor. However, all confusion should now cease since the sixth

Edition of the Standard Method of Measurement of Building Works now states in Clause A8 that the term 'provisional sum' shall be reserved for a sum provided for work or for costs which cannot be entirely foreseen, defined or detailed at the time when the tendering documents are issued. The term 'prime cost sum' is to be reserved for sums provided for work or services to be executed by a nominated sub-contractor, a statutory authority or public undertaking, or for materials or goods to be obtained from a nominated supplier. Clauses 27 and 28 of the JCT form of contract endorse this view.

## Method of billing

Some surveyors prefer to bill prime cost and provisional sums under section headings; for example, specialist floor tiling under 'Finishings', or iron-mongery under 'Woodwork'. The one advantage of this system is that the true value of the section can be seen from the total in the final summary. Another common method is to collect all the prime cost and provisional sums and bill them in a special section in the bills of quantities, usually at the end, under the heading of 'Prime Cost and Provisional Sums'. The advantages here are that there is very little possibility of a single item being overlooked during the pricing or settlement of the final account. Also, it is useful to be able to see at a glance the sum total of all the prime cost and provisional sums. Example G shows a typical arrangement of the billing of these sums.

## Adjustment in the variation account

### Nominated sub-contractors

Clause 30 (5) (c) of the JCT form states that the amounts paid or payable by the contractor to nominated sub-contractors (including the cash discount mentioned in Clause 27) shall be set against the prime cost or provisional sum in the contract bills. It also states that the balance, after the contractor's profit has been allowed *pro rata* at the rates shown in the contract bills, shall be added to or deducted from the contract sum.

### Example

The item for shopfronts shown in Example G may be taken as an illustration. It is assumed that the contractor had priced the profit item as 10%, and the attendance item as £200.00. If during the course of the contract the contractor was instructed to accept the estimate of 'Shopfronts Ltd' of £9800.00 for this work, the final account adjustment would be as follows:

*Example G: The Billing of Prime Cost and Provisional Sums*

| | | | | £ | p |
|---|---|---|---|---|---|
| | PRIME COST AND PROVISIONAL SUMS | | | | |
| | **NOMINATED SUB-CONTRACTORS** | | | | |
| | *The following sums are for work to be executed by Nominated Sub-Contractors, and include a cash discount of 2½% for the Contractor* | | | | |
| A | *Include the sum of* £10,000.00 *for the supply and fixing of a new shopfront complete* | | | 10,000 | 00 |
| B | Add for profit | % | | | |
| C | Add for general attendance as defined | | | | |
| | **NOMINATED SUPPLIERS** | | | | |
| | *The following sums are for materials and goods to be purchased from Nominated Suppliers, and fixed elsewhere in these bills of quantities by the Contractor. These sums include a cash discount of 5% for the Contractor* | | | | |
| D | Include the sum of £300.00 for the supply only of Ironmongery | | | 300 | 00 |
| E | Add for profit | % | | | |
| | **STATUTORY UNDERTAKERS** | | | | |
| | *The following sums are for work to be executed by the Local Authority, and are strictly net. The Contractor must include in his profit item for any loss of discount* | | | | |
| F | Include the sum of £150.00 for the making good to the public footpath | | | 150 | 00 |
| G | Add for profit | % | | | |
| H | Add for general attendance as defined | | | | |
| | **SUMS FOR ADDITIONAL WORKS** | | | | |
| | *The following sums are net, and are to be expended as directed by the Architect, or deducted in whole or in part, if not required* | | | | |
| I | Repairs to the existing structure | | | 500 | 00 |
| F | Contingencies | | | 1,000 | 00 |
| | *Total carried to Collection Page 114* | | £ | | |

*Shopfronts*

| | | Omissions | | Additions | |
|---|---|---|---|---|---|
| *Omit* | | £ | p | £ | p |
| The sum included for shopfronts: 92/A .. | | 10,000 | 00 | | |
| Profit 92/B.. .. .. .. .. .. | 5% | 500 | 00 | | |
| Attendance 92/C .. .. .. .. .. | | 200 | 00 | | |
| | | | | | |
| *Add* | | | | | |
| The accepted quotation of Shopfronts Ltd dated 29/10/79 .. .. .. .. .. | | | | 9,800 | 00 |
| Profit .. .. .. .. .. .. | 5% | | | 490 | 00 |
| Attendance .. .. .. .. .. | | | | 200 | 00 |
| | | 10,700 | 00 | 10,490 | 00 |
| | | 10,490 | 00 | | |
| *Net omission* £ | | 210 | 00 | | |

It should be noted that the contractor would probably issue a cheque for £9555.00 to Shopfronts Ltd to settle this account: that is, £9800.00 less 2½% discount. This, of course, would apply only if the contractor paid the account within the discount period, since the payment would otherwise be the full £9800.00. The sum of £210.00 would be carried to the final summary as a deduction from the contract sum in the computation of the final account.

*Profit adjustment*

The contract states that the profit shall be adjusted *pro rata* to the amount paid, including the cash discount. This would apply even if the profit had been entered as a lump sum in the priced bills of quantities and the percentage omitted from the rate column. The fact that the figure of £9800.00 may include authorized daywork and fluctuations charges for materials and labour does not affect this method of profit adjustment. Confusion often arises on this point, since Clause 31 states that fluctuations shall not alter in any way the amount of profit included in the contract sum. However, Clause 31 refers to the main contract and need not affect nominated sub-contractors, since the adjustment of such accounts is governed by Clauses 27, 30 (5) (c) and 31 D (5) (b).

*Attendance items*

Attendance on nominated sub-contractor's accounts is not adjusted *pro rata* to the amount paid, but depends upon the extent of the work done. Once a lump sum has been inserted it remains constant, even though the nominated sub-contractor's final account may be half or double the amount inserted in the bills of quantities; this is provided that the extent of the attendance work remains the same. For example, a certain sum may be included in a contract for the installation of two lifts. The architect may prefer the lifts to have more expensive electrical equipment and passenger cars, so that the sum inserted in the bills of quantities would thus be exceeded by half as much again. The contractor's profit would be adjusted *pro rata* to the increased amount, but, since the attendance work is exactly the same, the figure inserted in the bills of quantities would remain unchanged. Again, if one of the lifts were completely omitted, then the attendance item would be reduced in the final account.

Since the key to this question is always the amount of work done in attendance, it is more satisfactory if the attendance is priced as a lump sum. Some contractors insert a percentage in the rate column against this item, but before the contract is signed they should be asked to change this to a lump sum. If a percentage is accepted for an item of attendance, then the attendance must be adjusted *pro rata* to the amount paid in the final account. This is because if the attendance is left as a percentage when the contract is signed both parties intend the item to be adjusted *pro rata* to the amount paid.

Clause B9 of the Standard Method of Measurement (sixth Edition) states that two attendance items may be required for each nominated sub-contractor:

(a)  a general attendance item
(b)  a special attendance item (now termed 'other' attendance).

### General attendance

Although Clause B9.2 of the Standard Method of Measurement defines the term general attendance it is prudent to include this definition in the bills of quantities, either in the Preliminaries Bill or at the commencement of the Prime Cost and Provisional Sums Bill. A typical definition would be as follows: 'The term "General attendance" in these bills of quantities shall be deemed to include the granting of right and providing access to the works, allowing use of standing scaffolding, messrooms, sanitary accommodation and welfare facilities, providing space for office accommodation and for storage of plant and materials, providing light and water for their work, clearing away rubbish.'

### Other attendance

An item of special attendance if required must be given for nominated sub-contractors stating full particulars of the work involved, e.g. unloading, storing, hoisting, placing in position, providing power, providing special scaffolding (see S M M Clause B9.3).

### Cash discounts

The contractor's cash discount on nominated sub-contractor's accounts which are based upon an accepted net quotation can cause confusion, since these do not include a $2\frac{1}{2}$% cash discount for the main contractor as is laid down in the contract. This dilemma, however, is unnecessary since all invitations to proposed nominated sub-contractors should point out the provisions of Clause 27 (a), which sets out the agreement between the employer and the contractor concerning the basis on which nominated sub-contractor's quotations should be accepted. Furthermore, contractors can help to overcome this difficulty by checking that the correct discount provisions are made in quotations before they carry out the architect's instructions to accept them in writing. Nevertheless, if the contractor accepts a net quotation he may still deduct his contractual discount when paying the nominated sub-contractor's final account. The certificate of the architect is a condition precedent to payment of a nominated sub-contractor's account, and therefore the contractor is entitled to make the deduction provided for in Clause 27 (b) from any amount so certified. If, therefore, a sub-contractor who accepted nomination under Clause 27 failed to provide in the subcontract sum for the discount reserved to the contractor under his contract with the employer, the contractor could still make the authorised deductions from any amounts certified as due in respect of the subcontract works.

It is often difficult to decide whether a contractor is entitled to deduct $2\frac{1}{2}$% cash discount from the total amount of a nominated sub-contractor's account which includes charges for dayworks and fluctuations. Fluctuations in nominated sub-contractor's accounts are to be adjusted in accordance with Clause 30 (5) (c) of the JCT form of contract, cash discounts can therefore be deducted from the amount paid – that is, from the total amount including daywork and fluctuations. When difficulties arise on this point between nominated sub-contractors and main contractors some surveyors add $\frac{1}{39}$th to the daywork and fluctuations to compensate for the lost discount. This practice is not strictly correct, since it means that a cash discount, which must be earned by fulfilling certain conditions of payment, is converted into a certain reimbursement. Any discounts in excess of $2\frac{1}{2}$% cash discount are for the benefit of the employer.

The real answer to this problem would seem to be to include a suitable item in the preliminary section of the bills of quantities which will state clearly the procedure to be adopted in the final account. The contractor is then fully aware of the situation and can act accordingly, both in pricing the original tender and in accepting specialist quotations, and arguments on this technicality can be avoided.

*Employer paying direct*
Under Clause 27 (c) of the JCT form of contract the employer has the power to pay a nominated sub-contractor's account direct if the contractor defaults. In this case the contractor is not entitled to the cash discount, since this is valid only when he himself makes the payment, and then only if he pays within the stipulated time. The profit included in the priced bills of quantities

would still be allowed in the final account, *pro rata* to the amount actually paid by the employer.

*Contractor tendering for work covered by a prime cost or provisional sum*
Clause 27 (g) of the JCT form of contract states that where a contractor directly carries out work in the ordinary course of his business for which a prime cost or provisional sum has been included in the contract bills he must indicate in the Appendix to the conditions of contract that he wishes to tender for it. The question often arises whether the contractor is entitled to the profit inserted by him in the contract bills immediately after the provisional sum for such work, and to the cash discount that he would have received if another sub-contractor had carried out the work. This problem must be considered before the contractor is allowed to submit his price. His quotation must compare with others, and must therefore be based on the same conditions as a possible nominated sub-contractor; he should thus be entitled to the profit shown in the contract bills, *pro rata* to the accepted quotation.

Cash discount would not be allowed, as it would be impossible for the contractor to allow cash discount to himself. When the main contractor is invited to tender for such work he should be told whether his tender is to include for profit and attendance or whether his quotation is to be prepared on exactly the same lines as a nominated sub-contractor's would be. In this way no misunderstandings can arise.

### Nominated suppliers
Clause 30 (5) (c) of the JCT form of contract provides that the amounts paid or payable by the contractor to nominated suppliers (including the cash discount mentioned in Clause 28) shall be set against the prime cost or provisional sum in the contract bills; and the balance, after allowing *pro rata* for the contractor's profit at the rate shown in the priced bills of quantities, shall be added to or deducted from the contract sum.

### Example
Take the item for ironmongery shown in Example G (page 43) and assume that the contractor had priced the profit item at 10%. If during the course of the contract the contractor was instructed to accept the estimate of 'Lock and Bolt Ltd' of £360.000 for the supply of ironmongery the final account adjustment would be as shown on page 48.

In the settlement of this account the contractor would probably issue a cheque for £342.00 to Lock and Bolt Ltd – that is, £360.00 less 5% discount. This would apply only if the contractor paid the account within the discount period, since otherwise the payment would be £360.00. The sum of £66.00 would be carried to the final summary as an addition to the contract sum, when the final account is worked out.

*Ironmongery*

| | | Omissions | | Additions | |
|---|---|---|---|---|---|
| | | £ | p | £ | p |
| *Omit* | | | | | |
| The sum included for the supply of iron-mongery 92/D | | 300 | 00 | | |
| Profit 92/E .. .. .. .. .. .. | 10% | 30 | 00 | | |
| *Add* | | | | | |
| The accepted quotation of Messrs Lock and Bolt Ltd dated 5/11/79 .. .. .. .. | | | | 360 | 00 |
| Profit .. .. .. .. .. .. .. | 10% | | | 36 | 00 |
| | | 330 | 00 | 396 | 00 |
| | | | | 330 | 00 |
| | | | *Net addition* £ | 66 | 00 |

### Profit adjustment

Nominated sub-contractors' accounts are adjusted in the same way as those of nominated suppliers, as has just been described. Any changes that are made in the nominated supplier's account to cover authorized fluctuations are still dealt with under Clause 30 (5) (c) and not under Clause 31 of the JCT form of contract, and the contractor's profit would similarly be adjusted *pro rata* to the amount paid, which would include such fluctuation charges (see Clause 31 (D) (5) (b)).

### Cash discounts

The contractor's cash discount on nominated suppliers' accounts which are based upon accepted net quotations can cause confusion since these quotations do not include a cash discount for the general contractor as laid down in the contract. This dilemma, however, is unnecessary, since all invitations to nominated suppliers should point out the provisions of Clause 28 (a). This sets out the agreement between the employer and the contractor as to the basis on which nominated supplier's quotations should be accepted. Furthermore, contractors can help to overcome this difficulty by checking that the correct discount provisions are made in quotations before carrying out the instructions of the architect to accept them.

Clause 28 (b) (iv) places the onus on the architect by stating that the architect shall not nominate a supplier who will not allow the contractor a 5% discount for cash, if the contractor pays within 30 days of the end of the month in which the delivery is made. The employer can of course overcome this problem by making an allowance in lieu of the lost discount. This would mean a variation of the form of contract, which is quite permissible if both parties agree.

As in the case of nominated sub-contractors, the question often arises of whether the contractor is entitled to deduct a cash discount of 5% from the total value of a nominated supplier's account when that account contains authorized fluctuations. The contractor is entitled to do this but the procedure for dealing with this technical argument should be set out in the tendering documents as previously stated.

*Trade discounts*
All trade discounts, and any cash discounts in excess of 5%, are for the benefit of the employer. Clause 28 (a) states that the term 'prime cost' shall mean the net cost defrayed after deducting all trade discounts and other discounts except a cash discount of 5%.

*Delivery charges, packing and carriage*
Clause 28 (a) provides that the prime cost shall be inclusive of the cost of packing, carriage, and delivery to site. If the contractor has had to collect goods or materials from a nominated supplier's works, or from a nearby railhead, the collection costs would become part of the prime cost. The costs of the return of empty crates and packing cases are usually covered elsewhere in the contract bills, either as a part of the 'fixing item' or as a special item. Clause 28 (a) provides that where in the opinion of the architect the contractor has incurred expenses for special packing or special carriage, this shall be allowed as part of the sums actually paid by the contractor.

*Breakages and replacements*
Breakages that occur during transit to the site, before receipt by the contractor, are usually the liability of the supplier, but this depends on the conditions of the original quotation. Any breakages and replacements that occur after the contractor has received the materials or goods become the contractor's liability. When replacements are shown in the invoice they are not entered into the final account.

*Fixing of nominated supplier's materials*
The fixing of nominated supplier's materials or goods is usually given in the respective section for the item in the bills of quantities. It is advisable to define clearly the term 'fixing' in the bills of quantities, either in the preliminaries bill or at the beginning of the prime costs and provisional sums bill. This should leave no doubt in the contractor's mind as to the exact nature of the fixing item that he is pricing. A typical definition would be as follows: 'The term "fixing" in these bills of quantities shall be deemed to include taking delivery, off-loading, unpacking, checking of goods and invoices, notification of shortages and damage, providing safe storage, distributing on site, hoisting and fixing the materials in position, and returning all empty crates and packing cases free of charge to the Employer' (see SMM Clause B10.2).

### Example H: Methods of Billing Prime Cost Items

| | | | £ | p |
|---|---|---|---|---|
| **METHOD 1** | | | | |
| *Extract from Brickwork Bill* | | | | |
| Include the prime cost sum of £110.00 for the supply only of a wrought iron gate | Item | | 110 | 00 |
| Add for profit | Item | 5% | 5 | 50 |
| Fixing wrought iron gate size 900 × 2000 mm to brick reveals, including building in pair of lugs and gate catch to faced brickwork, and make good | 1 No. | £9.20 | 9 | 20 |
| **METHOD 2** | | | | |
| *Extract from Prime Cost and Provisional Sums Bill* | | | | |
| Include the sum of £110.00 for the supply only of a wrought iron gate | Item | | 110 | 00 |
| Add for profit | Item | 5% | 5 | 50 |
| Receive, unload, store, return all empty crates and packing cases, and pay all carriage charges | Item | | 3 | 50 |
| *Extract from Brickwork Bill* | | | | |
| Fixing wrought iron gate size 900 × 2000 mm to brick reveals, including building in pair of lugs and gate catch to faced brickwork, and make good | 1 No. | £8.50 | 8 | 50 |
| **METHOD 3** | | | | |
| *Extract from Brickwork Bill* | | | | |
| Wrought iron gate size 900 × 2000 mm (P.C. £110.00) and add for profit and fixing to brick reveals, including building in a pair of lugs and gate catch to faced brickwork, and make good | 1 No. | £124.70 | 124 | 70 |
| **METHOD 4** | | | | |
| *Extract from Brickwork Bill* | | | | |
| Extra over common brickwork, for facing externally in 65 mm sand-faced bricks (P.C. £60.00 per thousand) laid stretcher bond, pointed with a weather joint | 100 m$^2$ | £4.60 | 460 | 00 |

*Methods of billing prime cost items in bills of quantities*
Four methods of presenting a prime cost item in bills of quantities are commonly used today. These are shown in Example H. In methods 1 and 2 if the accepted quotation varies from the prime cost sum the profit is adjusted *pro rata* to the invoice amount, but the item for fixing in method 1, and the items for receiving, unloading, and so on, and fixing in method 2, remain the same. It is assumed in method 1 that the definition of the term 'fixing' includes for unloading, storing, and the return of empties and carriage charges.

   If in method 3 the accepted quotation varies from the prime cost sum included, it is difficult to assess the cost of the profit and fixing elements contained in the contractor's rate of £124.70. The quantity surveyor must adjust this item by confirming with the contractor the profit element that he had included in the rate. Failing this, the quantity surveyor must assess a fair profit, usually referring to other prime cost items in the bills of quantities. Given an accepted quotation and invoice of £121.00, a new rate would have to be built up as follows:

|  |  |  | £ | p |
|---|---|---|---|---|
| Messrs Lock and Bolt Ltd Invoice for the supply of a wrought iron gate as per the accepted quotation dated 5/11/79 |  |  | 121 | 00 |
| Add for profit 5% (confirmed with contractor) |  |  | 6 | 05 |

| Fixing costs | £ p | £ p |  |  |  |
|---|---|---|---|---|---|
| Original cost  ..    ..    .. | 110.00 | 124.70 | Fixing | | |
| Profit 5% ..    ..    ..    .. | 5.50 | 115 50 | costs | 9 | 20 |
|  | 115.50 | 9.20 |  |  |  |

|  |  | £ | p |
|---|---|---|---|
| *New rate* = | | 136 | 25 |

   In practice many surveyors avoid these petty calculations by adjusting this item in the final account on the basis of the net difference between the prime cost and the invoice cost. Although this method of net adjustment is not strictly correct, since the contract states that profit shall be adjusted *pro rata* to the amount paid, it often proves more practical.

   Probably methods 2 and 4 are now emerging as the most popular ways of billing such items.

   There appears to be no definite accepted method used by surveyors for adjusting such items as facing bricks and floor tiles, as set out in method 4. Three methods are set out here:

(a) To adjust the rate per square metre, based upon the prime cost and invoice prices, allowing for the requisite number of facing bricks per metre plus waste.

(b) To adjust the prime cost only, by omitting the prime cost sum, and adding back the invoice amount with profit adjustments, the profit element used being the profit included in other prime cost sums elsewhere in the bills of quantities.

(c) To adjust only the net difference between the two sums as an omission or addition as the case may be.

The following is an example of how method (a) could be applied to the item shown in Example H if the facing bricks used were actually invoiced at £65.00 per thousand, with the price of common bricks £30.00 per thousand, assuming fifty-nine bricks per square metre, plus one brick waste.

| *Breakdown of bill rate* | | *New rate* | |
|---|---|---|---|
| | £ | | £ |
| P.C. price | 60.00 | Invoice price | 65.00 |
| Commons | 30.00 | Commons | 30.00 |
| Extra cost = | 30.00 | Extra cost = | 35.00 |
| Therefore 60 = | 1.80 | Therefore 60 = | 2.10 |
| Bricks extra cost | 1.80 | Bricks extra cost | 2.10 |
| Profit, say 10% | 0.18 | Profit 10% | 0.21 |
| | 1.98 | | 2.31 |
| Bill rate | 4.60 | Extra labour, laying and pointing | 2.62 |
| Less bricks | 1.98 | | |
| | | New rate = | 4.93 |
| Extra labour, laying and pointing | 2.62 | | |

If a different type of brick were to be used instead—for example, handmade as against machine-made—this could affect the laying and pointing element of the cost, and also perhaps increase the waste. In this event a completely new rate should be agreed by means of a fair valuation, as set out in the provisions of Clause 11 (4) (b) of the JCT form of contract.

If method (b) were to be used the adjustment would be as follows:

| | Omissions | | Additions | |
|---|---|---|---|---|
| *Omit* | £ | p | £ | p |
| 6000 sand-faced bricks P.C. per 1000 .. | £60.00 | 360 00 | | |
| Profit on last confirmed from other P.C. item | 10% | 36 00 | | |
| *Add* | | | | |
| Invoice from the Clay Brick Co dated 12/12/77 per 6000 facing bricks .. .. .. | £65.00 | | 390 00 | |
| Profit .. .. .. .. .. .. | 10% | | 39 00 | |
| | | | 429 00 | |
| | | 396 00 | 396 00 | |
| | | Net addition 33 00 | | |

It will be seen that the waste element has been taken into account in this method; to face 100 m superficial, the net amount of bricks required would be 5,900. Therefore 100 bricks, waste, would appear to be a reasonable figure. This method of adjustment is more practical for this type of item and is the only one that can be used if the cost of the facing bricks varies during the course of the contract.

Method (c) is also used, but is not strictly correct, since it does not adjust the profit *pro rata* to the amount paid as laid down in the contract. It is often used, however, because of its simplicity.

### Statutory undertakers

Prime cost and provisional sums are often included in bills of quantities to cover the cost of work to be undertaken by Local Authority departments and nationalized industries. Since these are generally non-trading organizations, it is often impossible for them to offer discounts for cash payments. These undertakers are not strictly nominated sub-contractors, because the architect really has no choice in the matter; and they are governed by Clause 4 of the JCT form of contract, and not Clause 27. It is good practice to separate such prime cost and provisional sums in the bills of quantities which have been included for this type of work and to point out to tenderers that the sums are strictly net and that the loss of discount must be considered when the profit item is priced.

### Sums for additional works

Provisional sums are included in the bills of quantities to cover the cost of additional works usually carried out by the main contractor, the exact nature of which is not known when the tender is prepared. There is no provision in the bills of quantities for the addition of profit, since the main contractor will execute the works and be paid according to the rule set out in Clause 11 of the JCT form of contract.

Although the extent of the work is not known, it can often be described in the contract bills, and the quantity surveyor can estimate the sum before the tender is made. This is because architects prefer to insert a contingent sum of money which can be used in part or in full to pay for this type of additional work. Thus the employer need not constantly be asked to authorise small items of over-expenditure, which can be difficult if he is restricted by loan sanctions.

If the architect wished during the course of the contract to nominate a supplier or sub-contractor for this additional work the contractor would be entitled to a profit *pro rata* to the actual amount spent, based upon the profit included on similar provisional sums throughout the contract bills. If the provisional sum is related to normal building work the contractor could probably claim that the addition of the percentage profit should be the same as that included in his rates for measured work of this nature.

### Creation of prime cost and provisional sums

Unless the contractor agrees, the architect has no powers to create a prime cost or provisional sum for additional works after the contract is signed. By Clauses 27 and 28 of the JCT form of contract, only the items included in the contract bills may be adjusted in the manner prescribed. Therefore a contractor could insist that the additional work be measured and valued under Clause 11, as a normal variation.

### GC/Works/1 form of contract

Like the JCT form and the Standard Method of Measurement (Clause A8), Condition 38 of the GC/works/1 form states that the words 'prime cost' or the initials P.C. shall apply to nominated or appointed sub-contractors, and nominated or appointed suppliers. The term 'provisional sum' is reserved for net lump sums for work to be executed by the contractor, the exact nature of which is unknown at the time of tendering. In this form of contract the sums included for both nominated or appointed sub-contractors and nominated or appointed suppliers should include $2\frac{1}{2}\%$ cash discount for the main contractor. If, however, a net quotation is accepted by the main contractor, several Government departments rule that no allowance shall be made for the lost discount. In Government contracts work covered by P.C. items is usually the subject of a competitive tender from firms which may or may not have been selected originally by the employing authority.

This form of contract is also more explicit about the payment of the contractor's profit, should the employing authority exercise its right to order and pay prime cost sums direct. It provides that if the employing authority does elect to pay these sums direct the contractor's profit will be allowed *pro rata* to the amount paid. Moreover, this form of contract actually states in Condition 39 that if any work is carried out for which a provisional lump sum has been included, then the provisional lump sum shall be deducted from the contract sum, and the work shall be measured and valued in accordance with Condition 9.

# 6. Fluctuations

Before the Second World War practically all building contracts were arranged on a firm price basis. That meant that after the contract was signed it was the contractor and not the employer who was affected by fluctuations in wage rates and material. In an inflationary period such as the 1950s this would naturally be to the employer's advantage. On the other hand, the economic depression of the early 1930s encouraged contractors to make low tenders, anticipating further falls in prices; as the margin of profit was so low, the contractor often went bankrupt if prices held steady.

After the outbreak of the Second World War there was a big increase in building activity because of Government contracts for war projects. This, of course, meant a steady rise in wages and the price of materials. Many wartime contracts were carried out on a prime cost basis; that is, actual prime cost of labour and materials, plus either a fixed or percentage fee to cover overheads and profit. The rise in costs did not affect contractors, since increases were included in the prime cost; in fact, the higher the prime cost, the higher became the percentage type of fee.

Since more work was being carried out on this basis, it became necessary to make some provision in the more traditional types of building contracts. To overcome this difficulty the Government inserted a 'cost variation clause' in their standard form of contract GC/Works/1. This clause stated that in the event of any variations occurring in wage rates and materials prices after the contract was signed the net amount of such variation would be reimbursed to the contractor as an addition or deduction, as the case might be, from the contract sum. The principle soon became established that the contractor should not lose financially in the event of a rise in prices, but that he would not receive any increased profit or overheads. A similar clause, named the 'fluctuations clause', was introduced into the JCT form of contract.

The galloping inflation of the late 1940s and 1950s underlined the necessity of retaining these clauses in building contracts, and it appeared at one time that they had come to stay. In 1958 the Ministry of Works stated that they intended in future to let contracts of £100,000.00 and below on a firm price basis; this was to assist the Government drive to halt the inflationary spiral. Other Government departments, Local Authorities and private employers quickly followed suit and for some years the majority of contracts were let on this basis.

The extensive social legislation in the mid 1960s, which included heavy increases in National Insurance employers' contributions and the inception of the Selective Employment Tax, brought about the re-introduction of the fluctuation clause into many building contracts. Attempts to obtain limited firm-price tenders were helped during a period in the late 1960s and early 1970s when wage increases were negotiated to be phased over three-year stages. This method of wage negotiation was a great help to builders' estimators in their work as it meant that they were aware of the proposed wage increases and the dates on which they were due to take effect. When preparing firm-price tenders, estimators included approximate sums in their tenders to cover the cost of wage and material increases.

In the period 1973 to 1975, as inflation soared beyond the 25 per cent per annum mark, many contractors lost heavily on firm-price contracts, especially in respect of increases in the cost of materials. During that period it became the normal rule that all projects of over twelve months duration were to be on a fluctuating price basis. Contractors are currently reluctant to offer firm-price tenders for any work even of six months duration because of the uncertainty with future wage and material prices, although desperate competition can sometimes override this reluctance.

One of the less desirable features of fluctuations clauses has been the marked lack of resistance of contractors to suppliers, and suppliers to manufacturers, when prices increase. The return of the firm-price contract did make contractors endeavour to secure from suppliers firm-priced quotations for the term of the contract and thus resistance to price increase was set up right down the line of supply. Although in the past resistance to wage rises was not strong, the second principle emerged of agreeing on an operative date for wage increase up to and as far as nine months ahead.

### GC/Works/1 form

The fluctuations condition of the GC/Works/1 form of contract has been excluded from Edition 2. However, the fluctuations condition can be brought into a contract when certain conditions of value (at present £100,000 and over) and certain conditions of time (at present contracts exceeding one year's duration) are involved. This fluctuation condition would be available as a supplementary condition based on the NEDO Price Adjustment Formulae for Building Contracts.

### JCT form

Clauses 31A to F are the fluctuation clauses in the JCT form of contract (1963 Edition, 1977 Revision). Parts A, C, D and E should be used where the parties have agreed to follow fluctuations of the costs referred to in Parts A and C. Parts B, C, D and E should be used wherever Part A is not applicable and covers statutory types of fluctuations only. Part F is used where the parties have agreed that fluctuations should be dealt with by adjustment to tender price under the NEDO Price Adjustment Formulae for Building Contracts. Parts A, B, C, D ,and E should be deleted where Part F applies.

## *Labour*

### *Wages*

The provisions of Clause 31A are that the prices contained in the contract bills forming part of the contract, or the prices contained in the schedule of rates, as the case may be, are based upon the current rates of wages and other emoluments and expenses payable to the work-people engaged upon or in connection with the work, and are deemed to take into account any form of agreement which is announced at the date of tender to become operative at some future date. The wage rates and other emoluments and expenses are deemed to be those governed by the rules and decisions of the National Joint Council for the Building Industry or by some other body applicable to the works. If these wage rates and other emoluments and expenses are increased or decreased by reason of any alteration in the rules and decisions of these bodies made after the date of tender, then the net increase or decrease is to be added to or deducted from the contract sum accordingly. It is the contractor's duty to give written notice to the architect of any such changes within a reasonable time (See Clause 31D).

It will be seen from Clause 31A that it is not necessary for the actual wage rates and emolument to be stated on the basic price list, as are the rates for materials. The contract states clearly that these rates are deemed to be those current at the date of tender. Confusion has arisen on this point particularly among less experienced young surveyors who, having grasped that only the materials stated on the basic price list are eligible for fluctuation, have incorrectly extended this condition to the labour fluctuation claim.

Increases in wages that are given as a reward for increased output, or value of work, do not rank for claim under Clause 31. Annual increases to apprentices, or increases given to working foremen in recognition for service, are not therefore eligible for claim. Working foremen should be included with the appropriate trade in the fluctuations claim. A claim for a general foreman who has purely supervisory duties, and who is not producing work with his tools, should not be entered in the labour fluctuations claim because his wages are part of the contractor's overheads. The claim, on the other hand, that the foreman is 'engaged upon or in connection with the works' and so should rank under Clause 31 could be difficult to resist if there were evidence that his wage increased when a national wage award was made. This would prove that his wage rate was governed by the rules and decisions of the National Joint Council for the Building Industry.

As stated in a previous chapter, when daywork has been executed on a contract the actual rates paid should be charged in the daywork account (see Clauses 31D (5) and 11 (4) (c)). These hours should then be deducted from the fluctuations claim, so that the increase is not paid for twice. In practice the complicated records for increased costs of labour mean that many contractors are willing to forego this right and charge the daywork account at the basic rate. The cost of time spent in extracting the particular hours could amount to more than the sum gained in the daywork percentage of the increase. Nevertheless, the correct method is to charge the daywork account at current rates.

As far as fluctuations on overtime are concerned, increases or decreases are not allowed on the unproductive hours unless the employer has agreed. Strictly speaking a contractor is able to claim labour fluctuations on the actual hours worked during overtime only, if he has obtained authorization to work overtime. However, in practice and equity such fluctuations are usually paid, provided that the employer is not called upon to pay for fluctuations on a greater number of hours than he would have done had the work been carried out during normal working time. These difficulties should all be resolved before overtime begins by obtaining the necessary permission and clarifying the position as to fluctuations on the unproductive time.

Fluctuations in the cost of labour under Clause 31 cannot properly be claimed on maintenance work arising out of the contract when such work is the liability of the contractor and not chargeable to the employer. If the employer takes responsibility for the work it is not strictly maintenance but becomes extra work to the contract executed during the maintenance period, and in this case fluctiations can be claimed.

Clause 15 (2) of the JCT form of contract states that defects not in accordance with the contract must be made good at the contractor's expense, unless the architect directs otherwise. Clause 31 gives effect to fluctuations in cost on the contract sum. Maintenance work is really the making good of defects on work already executed in the contract sum, on which fluctuations will probably have been already allowed; since maintenance items are not admitted as part of the contract sum, Clause 31 does not apply.

Clause 31 states that the basic rates for wages shall be deemed to be those current at the date of tender. In the past contractors have found difficulty in having to make last-minute adjustments to tender prices to cover for increases in wages and materials before the date for the delivery of a tender. This has now been clarified by Clause 31 D (6) (a) which states that the expression 'date of tender' means the date ten days before that fixed for the employer to receive tenders.

*Employer's Liability and Third Party Insurance*
One of the effects of increases in wages is the corresponding increase in premiums paid by contractors to insurance companies to cover the risk of claims through Employer's and Third Party Liabilities. This is because the premiums are usually based upon a percentage of the annual wages paid by the contractor. Clause 31A recognizes the validity of such claims by specifically mentioning Employer's Liability Insurance and Third Party

Insurance as an expense within the meaning of the clause. Earlier editions of the form of contract contained no reference to these premiums; in order to overcome subsequent difficulties, the actual words Employer's Liability Insurance and Third Party Insurance were added. The contractor should substantiate such a claim with evidence of the percentage of wages that he actually pays to obtain insurance cover.

*Other emoluments and expenses*
Clause 31A (a) specifically states that any fluctuations occurring in other emoluments and expenses governed by the rules and decisions of the National Joint Council for the Building Industry shall be adjusted in accordance with the provisions of this clause. This means that any official changes in Working Rule 3 regarding extra payments to operatives would be admissible as a claim under Clause 31A. An example of this would be changes in Working Rule 3D for Tool Allowances.

Changes in Holidays with Pay contributions have always been recognized under the JCT form of contract as an emolument paid to work-people by the contractor (see Clause 31A (a)) 'Holiday Credits'. The wording of fluctuations clauses in other forms of contract should be studied very carefully on this point in the light of the decision of the Court of Appeal in the case of London County Council *v.* Henry Boot and Sons Ltd. Their Lordships allowed this appeal, since they held that weekly sums paid by Henry Boot and Sons Ltd in respect of holidays with pay were not included in the expression 'rates of wages payable' used in the LCC form of contract. Viscount Simonds said that there was no doubt that what the workman got from the operation of the holidays agreement was a benefit to him; it might loosely be called part of his remuneration. But it seemed to His Lordship an essential element in a 'wage' that it should be paid to the workman for work done by him, and it was just that element which was lacking in the holiday credit scheme. It was neither paid by the employer to the workman, nor related to the work which he did for the employer.

*Statutory contributions and taxes*
It will be seen that Clauses 31A (b) and 31B (a) are virtually identical and deal with fluctuations in relation to labour costs arising from subsequent Government legislation under an Act of Parliament. The major difference between Clauses 31A and 31B with regard to labour fluctuations is that Clause 31B covers fluctuation arising from Government legislation only, whereas Clause 31A covers fluctuation in labour costs arising from both Government legislation and agreement arising from national negotiation and agreement from within the industry. The parties to the contract agree upon the alternative required and strike out the unwanted clause.

Both Clause 31A (b) (i) (ii) and 31B (a) (i) (ii) state that the prices contained in the Contract Bills are deemed to be based upon rates of contribution, levies and taxes operative at the date of tender, or deemed to have been foreseen at that date. As mentioned previously clause 31D (6) (a) states that this should be a date ten days before the date fixed for the receipt of tenders by the employer. The criteria for 'deemed to have foreseen' is that the change of rate and the date of its commencement was fixed by Act of Parliament at the date of tender.

This applies not only to changes in existing legislation (e.g. change in employers' contribution to National Insurance), but also applies to any new type of tax or change introduced by legislation during the contract period (e.g. the introduction of the Selective Employment Tax Scheme in 1967). The abolition of SET in 1973 was responsible for extensive decreases on contracts which had included this tax.

### Industrial Training Act, levies and grant

The financial transactions arising under the Industrial Training Act 1964 are mentioned under Clauses 31A (b) (ii) and 31B (a) (ii). The standard form of contract specifically excludes these transactions from the fluctuations clause, no doubt because of the complicated accountancy involved arising from the levies and a multitude of grants. However, although the standard form advises against the inclusion of this Act, parties to a contract who mutually agree to include such transactions, are free to vary the standard form if they so wish.

### National Health Insurance

This scheme is not now specifically mentioned in the JCT form as was the case in the 1963 Edition. Clauses 31A (b) (i) (ii) and 31B (a) (i) (ii) cover fluctuations in employers' contribution to this scheme.

### Approved sub-contractors

Clause 31C states that the contractor shall incorporate in any subcontract he enters into, in respect of any portion of the works so sublet, provisions similar to those contained in the main contract. This relates to fluctuations caused by Acts of Parliament only if Clause 31B is used, but would cover fluctuation of wages and other emoluments and expenses in addition to statutory increases if Clause 31A is used.

If Clause 31A is used then fluctuations in wage rates, emoluments and expenses authorised by the body governing the rules and conditions of the particular trade of the approved sub-contractor will be adjusted accordingly. This provision is covered by Clause 31A (a) (i) which says that 'rates of wages and other emoluments and expenses governed by the rules and decisions of some other body, other than the National Joint Council for the Building Industry, in accordance with the rules and decisions of such other body applicable to the works, and current at the date of tender'.

### Nominated sub-contractors

As mentioned in a previous chapter, fluctuations in nominated sub-contractors' accounts are not covered by the provisions of Clause 31A or 31B but are dealt with under Clause 27 (see also Clause 31D (5) (b)).

*Manufactured joinery*

A claim for labour fluctuations is often made when a contractor has obtained manufactured joinery from a supplier who is not a nominated supplier, and the joinery manufacturer claims labour fluctuations for making the joinery items under the terms of his agreement with the contractor.

If the contractor had manufactured the joinery in his own workshops he would be entitled to claim the labour fluctuations. Although the joinery manufacturer only supplied the joinery to the contractor, he will have expended labour on its manufacture, which in principle is equivalent to the labour that the contractor would have had to use if he had made the joinery himself. This labour cost, however expended, is presumably included in the rates for the measured work tendered for by the contractor. It would appear that in such cases authorized increases in rates of wages paid in the manufacture of the joinery may be properly allowed under Clause 31A but suitable clauses should be included in the tendering documents to cover this point.

*Recording claims under Clause 31*

There is now a specific provision in Clause 31D (4) to fix the time for the payment of sums due to the contractor from claims arising under this clause: they are to be included in interim certificates.

It is far more satisfactory to have claims presented for checking at regular intervals throughout the contract period; the checking of fluctuations claims is tedious and laborious and is better taken in small doses. It is difficult for surveyors and their clerks to be accurate when they are faced all at once with a mountain of sheets supporting claims.

Contractors should submit claims for fluctuations together with supporting time sheets; it is good practice to have the time sheets signed for this purpose by the clerk of works at the end of each week. The clerk of works' signature does not mean that he has checked the arithmetic, but certifies that the work-people listed have actually worked on the site for the number of hours stated. Surveyors can often bring pressure to bear on a slack contractor at this point by instructing the clerk of works to refuse his signature on claim sheets more than two weeks late.

Many contractors have specially designed claim sheets printed for making claims under Clause 31, which reduce to a minimum the amount of clerical work involved in checking. Often provision is made for the names, grade, and hourly rate of the work-people to be entered on the sheet; if the clerk of works can certify these hours as correct it is possible to dispense with the supporting time sheets unless any difficulty arises. Progressive totals should be made of the amount due, so that a final total can be agreed immediately after the practical completion date. Example I is a typical fluctuations claim sheet.

*Example 1: Labour Fluctuations Claim Sheet*

| | AB CONSTRUCTION LTD, LEEDS | | LABOUR FLUCTUATIONS CLAIM SHEET | |
|---|---|---|---|---|

Contract

Week Ending

| Works No | Workman's Name | Grade | Rate | Basic Rates | | | | | | | Craftsmen | Increase Total | | Labourers | Remarks |
|---|---|---|---|---|---|---|---|---|---|---|---|---|---|---|---|
| | | | | S | M | T | W | T | F | S | Total | £ | p | | Brought Forward |
| | | | | | | | | | | | | | | | |
| | | | | | | | | | | | | | | | |
| | | | | | | | | | | | | | | | |
| | | | | | | | | | | | | | | | |
| | | | | | | | | | | | | | | | |
| | | | | | | | | | | | | | | | |
| | | | | | | | | | | | | | | | |
| | | | | | | | | | | | | | | | |
| | | | | | | | | | | | | | | | |

Hours Worked and Rates Certified Correct

Signed.............. Clerk of Works
Date...............

Signed.............. Site Agent
Date...............

Amount Certified
Signed.............. Quantity Surveyor
Date...............

*Materials*

*The basic price list*
The provisions of Clause 31A (c) refer to materials and are as follows:

(1) The prices contained in the contract bills are deemed to be based upon the materials prices specified in the basic price list attached to the bills of quantities.

(2) The prices entered in the basic price list are deemed to be the market prices for the materials current at the date of tender.

If during the progress of the contract the market prices of any of the materials specified in the basic price list should vary from those specified, then the net difference between the basic price and the market price payable by the contractor and current at the time when such materials are purchased shall be added to or deducted from the contract sum, as the case may be. In the event of any change in the market prices of any of the materials specified in the basic price list it is the contractor's duty to give written notice to the architect of such an event taking place, within a reasonable time (see Clause 31D (1) (d)).

Clause 31A (c) makes provision for the adjustment of fluctuations in the basic prices caused by normal operations of the market as supply and demand. In addition the clause specifically mentions that the term 'market prices' is deemed to include fluctuation occurring because of Government legislation under an Act of Parliament causing changes in tax, import purchase, sale, appropriation and the processing of materials.

It will be seen from the contract that only those items specified in the basic price list are eligible for adjustment under this clause. Any claim for the adjustment of a material that does not appear on the basic price list would be inadmissible. Once the contract is signed, the basic price list becomes a contract document, and therefore cannot be amended by either party, unless by mutual agreement. A blank basic price list is often incorporated in the bills of quantities when tenders are invited, and tenderers are instructed to enter the materials and their market prices for which they may wish to have adjustments made. When Local Authorities invite tenders they sometimes themselves enter the materials on the basic price list, leaving the tenderers to insert the basic prices. This is usually done to keep such adjustments to a minimum. If it is confined to the major materials it means that tenders are more uniform. For this same reason some Local Authorities send out basic price lists with tender documents which have the materials and prices already entered; this provides a better basis for the comparison of tenders, as well as restricting the materials to be adjusted.

The disadvantage of this method is that it assumes the smaller contractors can buy their materials at the same prices as the larger contracting organizations. It is not a good policy to invite tenders on this basis, since it means the employer is interfering in the contractor's buying policy, and he

## Example J: Basic Price List of Materials and Goods

*Basic price list of materials and goods*

Variations of the contract sum in accordance with clause *31A(c)(i) or *31B(b)(i) of the Conditions of Contract will only be permitted for the materials and goods listed below.

To enable adjustments to be made in the final account, caused by the possible fluctuation in the prices of materials, the Contractor shall insert below, the basic prices (current market prices) upon which his tender is computed. The materials inserted shall be limited to these materials which form an important element of the contract, and *bona fide* quotations for these materials must be produced, before the signing of the contract.

Vouchers and invoices must be furnished in support of any adjustments, and only the net fluctuation in prices will be taken into account. Any difference between the basic prices and the prices payable, which are due to purchasing in small quantities, or any other cause other than genuine market fluctuation will not be the subject of adjustment. Written notice of all price fluctuations must be given to the Architect as they arise.

| Materials or Goods Delivered to Site | Unit | Basic Price |
|---|---|---|
| | | |

*Delete whichever is inapplicable

very often obtains benefits from this freedom of the contractor. The uniformity gained in tenders, moreover, does not necessarily apply to the ultimate final account, which, after all, is the true cost of the building. When this system is used the wording of the JCT standard form of contract will have to be amended before the contract is signed, since Clause 31A (c) states that the contractor shall state on the basic price list the prices of materials. Example J shows a typical basic price list.

*Checking the basic price list*
The surveyor should scrutinize carefully the basic price list submitted by the successful tenderer. Any errors that are overlooked at this stage could make an appreciable difference to the final account. The surveyor should satisfy himself that the basic prices are realistic, and obtain original estimates from the contractor to verify the basic prices. He should carefully check that the prices are all for materials actually delivered to the site, and endorse the basic price list if an ex-works price is quoted. Cash discounts on supporting quotations should be checked to make sure that they are in accordance with normal business practice. Discount calculations should be eliminated from the adjustment of prices by ensuring that the materials will be invoiced with the same discount provisions, thus cancelling one another out.

*Preparation of a statement for materials' fluctuations*
Clause 31A does not state who shall prepare the statement of fluctuations, but Clause 11 states that the surveyor shall prepare a bill of variations. It would appear, therefore, that, strictly speaking, it is the surveyor's duty to prepare such a statement. Very often in practice the contractor draws up a claim for materials' fluctuations, and submits this to the surveyor for checking, along with all the supporting invoices. If the contractor fails to do this the surveyor would have to obtain all the necessary invoices from him so that he could prepare the statement himself.

Because of the complex work involved, it is now common practice to find that the tendering contractors will not fill in the details for submission at the tender date and will write 'Full details to be submitted and agreed if this tender is successful'. This would seem to be a reasonable procedure.

All the materials listed on the basic price list must be adjusted, and all invoices for every material appearing on the list must be submitted. Even if the purchase price and the basic price have not varied, the item must be shown in the fluctuations claim statement as nil, to show that the material has not simply been overlooked. This type of statement is best prepared on a tabulated basis in the interests of tidiness. Examples K and L show two possible methods of dealing with such a statement. The method used in Example K is suitable for a small contract, where all the fluctuations can be calculated with the total number of invoices for the particular material to

*Example K: Materials' Fluctuations Claim Sheet*

*Contract:* Wood Lane Grammar School

| Material | Common Bricks | | | Basic price £28.00 *per* 1000 | | |
|---|---|---|---|---|---|---|
| *Supplier* | *Invoice* | | | *Amount* | | |
| | *Date* | *No.* | *Quantity* | *Rate* | £ | *p* |
| LBC LTD | 1/10/77 | Z1599 | 10,000 | £30.00 | 300 | 00 |
| ,, | 3/10/77 | Z1762 | 10,000 | £30.00 | 300 | 00 |
| ,, | 8/10/77 | Y15 | 12,500 | £30.00 | 375 | 00 |
| ,, | 12/10/77 | Y86 | 7,500 | £30.00 | 225 | 00 |
| WESTWOODS LTD | 14/10/77 | 29984 | 10,000 | £30.05 | 300 | 50 |
| ,, | 16/10/77 | 30042 | 7,000 | £30.05 | 210 | 35 |
| LBC LTD | 20/10/77 | Y232 | 12,000 | £30.10 | 361 | 20 |
| ,, | 26/10/77 | Y333 | 6,000 | £30.10 | 180 | 60 |
| ,, | 30/10/77 | Y454 | 7,500 | £30.00 | 225 | 00 |
| ,, | 1/11/77 | Y473 | 7,000 | £30.00 | 210 | 00 |
| ,, | 4/11/77 | Y522 | 6,000 | £30.05 | 180 | 30 |
| WESTWOODS LTD | 8/11/77 | 31192 | 6,500 | £30.00 | 195 | 00 |
| ,, | 12/11/77 | 33390 | 7,000 | £30.05 | 210 | 35 |
| ,, | 14/11/77 | 34229 | 6,500 | £30.00 | 195 | 00 |
| ,, | 18/11/77 | 34922 | 10,000 | £30.05 | 300 | 50 |
| ,, | 29/11/77 | 42293 | 3,500 | £30.00 | 105 | 00 |
| | | | 129,000 | | 3873 | 80 |
| | LESS BASIC | | 129,000 | £28.00 | 3612 | 00 |
| | *Net addition carried to summary* | | | £ | 261 | 80 |

hand. The method used in Example L can be used for contracts where the fluctuations are being calculated during the progress of the contract, when running totals can be used for interim certificate purposes.

*Checking the materials' fluctuations statement*
When the materials' fluctuations claim is complete the surveyor must extract the total quantity of each material from the statement, and then check that the quantities claimed are reasonable for the amount of work in the contract. This can be done by taking the quantities given in the bills and allowing for subsequent variations, thus estimating the amount of each material. For example, total quantities are extracted for concrete in each of the various

*Example L: Materials Fluctuations Claim Sheet*

| Contract: Wood Lane Grammar School | Invoice | | Quantity | Material | Common Bricks | | | Basic price £28.00 per 1000 | | | |
|---|---|---|---|---|---|---|---|---|---|---|---|
| | | | | | | | | Omission | | Addition | |
| Supplier | Date | No. | Quantity | Basic price | Invoice price | Increase | Decrease | £ | p | £ | p |
| LBC LTD | 1/10/77 | Z1599 | 10,000 | £28.00 | £30.00 | 2.00 | — | | | 20 | 00 |
| ,, | 3/10/77 | Z1762 | 10,000 | £28.00 | £30.00 | 2.00 | — | | | 20 | 00 |
| ,, | 8/10/77 | Y15 | 12,500 | £28.00 | £30.00 | 2.00 | — | | | 25 | 00 |
| ,, | 12/10/77 | Y86 | 7,500 | £28.00 | £30.00 | 2.00 | — | | | 15 | 00 |
| WESTWOODS LTD | 14/10/77 | 29984 | 10,000 | £28.00 | £30.05 | 2.05 | — | | | 20 | 50 |
| ,, | 16/10/77 | 30042 | 7,000 | £28.00 | £30.05 | 2.05 | — | | | 14 | 35 |
| LBC LTD | 20/10/77 | Y232 | 12,000 | £28.00 | £30.10 | 2.10 | — | | | 25 | 20 |
| ,, | 26/10/77 | Y333 | 6,000 | £28.00 | £30.10 | 2.10 | — | | | 12 | 60 |
| ,, | 30/10/77 | Y454 | 7,500 | £28.00 | £30.00 | 2.00 | — | | | 15 | 00 |
| ,, | 1/11/77 | Y473 | 7,000 | £28.00 | £30.00 | 2.00 | — | | | 14 | 00 |
| ,, | 4/11/77 | Y522 | 6,000 | £28.00 | £30.05 | 2.05 | — | | | 12 | 30 |
| WESTWOODS LTD | 8/11/77 | 31192 | 6,500 | £28.00 | £30.00 | 2.00 | — | | | 13 | 00 |
| ,, | 12/11/77 | 3390 | 7,000 | £28.00 | £30.05 | 2.05 | — | | | 14 | 35 |
| ,, | 14/11/77 | 34229 | 6,500 | £28.00 | £30.00 | 2.00 | — | | | 13 | 00 |
| ,, | 18/11/77 | 34922 | 10,000 | £28.00 | £30.05 | 2.05 | — | | | 20 | 50 |
| ,, | 29/11/77 | 42293 | 3,500 | £28.00 | £30.00 | 2.00 | — | | | 7 | 00 |
| | | | | | Net Addition Carried to Summary | | | | | £261 | 80 |

mixes, and from this the amount of cement can be calculated. To this will be added the amount of cement in mortar extracted from the brickwork quantities, and after a fair allowance for waste has been made the total amount of cement should compare reasonably well with the total quantity of cement claimed for fluctuations.

If the market price of a material should fluctuate when the contract is half completed, the whole of the invoices for that material should be submitted, even though half of the amount will be invoiced at basic prices. The total quantities of material can be checked only if this procedure is followed, since it ensures that any material used by the contractor on other contracts is not claimed for fluctuations on the contract in question.

### Change of material

It should be noted that under the fluctuations clause the only materials to be adjusted are those which appear on the basic price list; it is not correct practice to set the basic cost of one material against the purchase price of another, though similar, material. For example, sulphate-resisting cement cannot be adjusted against ordinary Portland cement. This change of material should be adjusted as a variation and dealt with under the provisions of Clause 11; thus the contractor receives the benefit of increased overhead and profit charges in the new rate, rather than the net difference in cost as in Clause 31A (c) (ii). Sometimes it may be simpler to set the price of the varied material against the basic price, but only with the agreement of both parties. Prices must be for strictly comparable materials; if, for instance, the basic price of cast iron drain pipes is for pipes in 3 m lengths, an invoice for such pipes in 4 m lengths cannot be set against that rate.

### Small quantities

Difficulties sometimes arise when materials are bought locally by the foreman. The invoices will show the retail prices for small quantities, and cannot be set against the basic price list. This is because Clause 31A (c) (i) refers to the possible variation of market prices which could not affect the higher retail prices of small quantities. This is often pointed out in the preamble to the basic price list.

### Materials from stock

The position may be complicated when a contractor supplies materials which he had bought some time ago for a sum lower than the basic price or the current market price. The contractor would make a loss if he replaced these materials at current prices; also, the capital invested in the goods would be unproductive, and he will have paid storage costs. This would seem a good reason for allowing the current market price to be set against the basic price, but Clause 31A (c) (ii) refers to 'the market price payable by the contractor and current when such materials and goods are bought'. This appears to preclude a fluctuations claim in such a case. It is possible, however, that the contractor knew when he made the tender that he held this particular material in stock and priced the item accordingly.

## *Fluctuations on timber for formwork*
When a basic price for timber has been entered in the basic price list fluctuations should be allowed in respect of timber used in formwork. This is because timber used in formwork should be regarded as consumable stores and not as plant. The value of timber salvaged by the contractor should be taken into account when the fluctuations claim is assessed.

## *Items of plant*
A material used by the contractor during construction, but not incorporated in the finished building, should not be entered on the basic price list. For example, if scaffolding had been entered on the basic price list by a contractor he should be asked to remove any such entry before the contract is signed.

## *Nominated suppliers*
Fluctuations on goods supplied by a nominated supplier are not dealt with under Clause 31, but are adjusted entirely under the provisions of Clause 28 (see chapter 5). In the JCT form this is confirmed in Clause 31D (5) (b).

## *Nominated sub-contractors*
Fluctuations on goods supplied and fixed by a nominated sub-contractor are not dealt with under Clause 31, but are adjusted entirely under the provisions of Clause 27 (see chapter 5). In the JCT form this is confirmed by Clause 31 D (5) (b).

## *Approved sub-contractors*
Clause 31C states that the contractor shall incorporate in any subcontract he enters into in respect of any portion of the works so sublet similar provisions to those contained in the main contract which relate to the fluctuation of materials. The materials used by approved sub-contractors should be entered on the basic price list, together with their basic prices. If the market price of any of the materials used by a sub-contractor which is specified in the basic price list fluctuates the net difference between the basic price and the market price payable by the sub-contractor shall be added to or deducted from the contract sum.

## *Statutory duties and taxes*
As stated previously, Clause 31A (c) makes provision for the fluctuation of prices caused by normal market conditions and for fluctuations caused by Government legislation under an Act of Parliament.

The alternative, Clause 31B (b), is used when fluctuations are to be restricted to those caused by Government legislation only. When this alternative clause is used it is only necessary to list the materials to which the clause is to apply and no prices are inserted against the items. This is known as the basic list.

Similar wording is used to that in the labour Clause 31 B (a) (ii) with regard to changes foreseen at the date of tender. The clause also mentions the introduction of any new type of rate, duty or tax affecting the price of materials

### Clauses 31E and 31F

Clause 31E was introduced in 1973 to recompense contractors for the high administration costs incurred in preparing and submitting claims for fluctuations. The actual percentage included for 31E is usually decided by the client's advisers and should be added to the total amount of the additions and omissions in respect of fluctuations.

Clause 31F was introduced in 1975 to provide a formula price adjustment for fluctuations in costs of labour, materials, plant, overheads, etc. The system and application is based on the Formula Rules laid down in the NEDO Price Adjustment Formulae for Building Contracts, using indices as opposed to the laborious traditional methods of recovery of fluctuations described earlier in this chapter. The use of 31F would be a decision for the client's advisers and Clauses 31A–E would then be deleted. Initially many contractors viewed this system with some suspicion, but currently there appears to be a reluctance by many employers to use 31F as it would seem to favour the contractor.

# 7. Valuations for interim certificates

## JCT form

Clause 30 of the JCT form of contract provides for interim certificates so that payment can be made on account. Without such a clause the contractor would not receive any payment until he had completed the contract. This would be an 'entire contract', in which one party must fulfil all his part of the contract before he can ask the other to carry out any of his part.

The heavy financial outlay of modern building contracts means that provision must be made for payment by instalments. Even the employer benefits from this, since the heavy interest charges on the money required to finance a large contract would be reflected in the contract sum.

Clause 30 of the JCT form of contract makes provision for the parties to agree the period of interim certificates by competing the necessary space in the appendix. A certificate, when used in relation to a building contract is a formal written document by which the architect certifies payments to the contractor. When the contractor receives a certificate he presents it to the employer and has a right to payment within the period stipulated in the contract.

Clause 30 (1) states that 'Interim valuations shall be made whenever the architect considers them necessary'. This means the contractor may demand a certificate at the set time; it does not matter whether the architect decides a valuation should be made for that certificate or not. The surveyor usually prepares a valuation and recommends to the architect the sum which should be certified. It is the duty of the architect actually to issue the certificate. It may be true that he has no real discretion as to the amount of a certificate once the quantity surveyor has determined the value. However, he has the right to determine whether any part of the value of the work should be excluded, if it has not been properly executed, or whether any part of the value of materials on the site should be excluded because they have been brought on to the site unreasonably, improperly, or prematurely.

When the surveyor makes his valuation he must make sure that it covers the sum to which the contractor is entitled, but that it is not more than the employer is liable to pay. The purpose of an interim certificate is to allow the contractor to receive a payment on account; it gives the approximate value of the work done or the materials delivered.

An interim certificate only establishes the sum certified, and not the adequacy of the work performed. When a certificate is issued it creates a debt due, and the contractor is entitled to payment in accordance with the terms of the contract, subject to the right of the employer to set off or counter-claim for liquidated damages.

Clause 30(1) states that the contractor shall be entitled to payment from the employer 'within fourteen days from the presentation of that certificate'.

### Contents of a valuation for certificate purposes

Clause 30(2) and (2A) lays down how the amount due shall be calculated. Many surveyors have special printed forms for this purpose, as shown in Example M. A valuation should always include the total value of work properly executed to date. This includes the value of any variations, materials and goods supplied by nominated suppliers and fixed by the contractor; work executed by nominated sub-contractors; the value of materials delivered to the site for use in the works, less the agreed retention; plus any fluctuations claims due. From this sum total is deducted the amount paid under any previous certificates. This should be done very carefully, since serious errors can be made which can easily be carried through to the final certificate.

### Preliminaries

Items priced in the preliminaries section of the bills of quantities can often form a major part of the work done in the early stages of the contract, and it is only right they should therefore be included in a certificate valuation. One method of determining the amount to be included is to proportion the preliminaries total against the contract period. For example, where the preliminaries total £15,000.00 for a fifty-week contract period the amount included would be £300.00 per week. Another method used is to proportion the preliminaries total against the contract amount, less the total of preliminaries. In both these methods any prime cost and provisional sums included in the preliminaries bill, such as contingency items, or sums included for possible dayworks, should be deducted before proportioning.

It will be seen, however, that neither method is entirely accurate. The first does not take into account that work may be behind programme, so that the complete preliminaries costs may be paid to the contractor before the work is completed. In both methods certain lump-sum preliminary items, such as site fencing and temporary roads, will be inadequately valued because they have to be completed early. Furthermore, such items as drying out the building and clearing away on completion will be included in part prematurely.

When initial works such as temporary site fencing, roads, hoardings, site huts, and welfare buildings are completed they should be included in the valuation in full. An allownce should first be deducted for maintenance and final removal. All lump-sum advance payments which must be made before work can be started should also be included in valuations in full. The contractor, for example, may have to make full payment for the water supply

## Example M: Valuation for Interim Certificates

*Pro forma for valuation for interim certificate purposes*

*Quantity Surveyor*                                              *Architect*

J. Jones, FRICS, FIQS
10 High Street,
Westford.

*Contract*...........................                        *Date*..................

*Name of Contractor*............................         *Valuation No.*...................

*Address*...............................................................

(1) Estimated Total Value of Builder's Work as Contract

                £ p £ p

  (a) Preliminaries
  (b) Substructure
  (c) Drainage
  (d) Siteworks
  (e) Superstructure

           *Total* £

(2) *Estimated Value of Variations to Date  Omit/Add*

(3) *Value of Nominated Suppliers' Goods Supplied*
  *Plus Profit*

(4) *Value of Nominated Sub-Contractors' Work to*
  *Date Plus Profit and Attendances*

(5) *Estimated Value of Materials on Site*
                £

(6) *Deduct Retention*
                £

(7) *Fluctuations under Clause 31\**     £ p
  (not subject to retention)
  (a) Wages, emoluments and expenses
  (b) Materials

         £

*Deduct Total of Previous Certificates*   £

    *Amount Recommended for Certification* £

\*If a percentage was added per Clause 31E or if 31F was used, the total of fluctuations would be
subject to normal retention.

before it can be connected. Items such as plant and scaffolding should be brought into the valuation in part or in full as applicable; completion items such as cleaning out and drying the building should be included at completion. Other preliminary items, such as foremen, site telephones, and other costs which carry on through the whole period of the contract, as well as sums retained for the maintenance of site hutting, should be proportioned to the amount of the contract or the contract period. It should be remembered that the initial stages of opening up a site are invariably most expensive and the contractor should have the full financial benefit of early payment for preliminary items as executed.

If, however, the preliminary bill is priced as a lump sum, or as a percentage, each item cannot be considered individually. In this case it is advisable to ask the contractor whose tender is being considered to give a detailed breakdown for every item priced in the preliminaries bill; this will also be to the contractor's advantage. If this step is not taken, the amount allowed in the valuation must be proportionate to the amount of the contract, or the contract period.

### Work executed as contract

The surveyor should inform the contractor when he intends to visit the site to prepare his valuation, so that the contractor's surveyor can be present, and make sure no work is overlooked. The contractor's surveyor can often be very helpful, since he usually spends more time on the site than the quantity surveyor.

When the contract is for a single building it is often easier to consider each item in the contract bills, to check if the work is complete. It can then be included in total in the valuation. When an item is only partially complete it may be simpler to measure the quantity completed on the site with a tape and rod. If it is more advanced, however, the amount remaining to be completed can be measured from the drawings and deducted from the amount in the contract bills. It is very useful to have a special set of drawings, usually only plans and elevations, and to mark in different colours the work done during the period of each valuation. From these drawings the amount of work completed can be rapidly measured in the site office; as the building nears completion this process can be reversed, so that the contract amount is taken and deductions made for work still to be executed.

Provisional quantities and any extensive re-measured sections of work can be abstracted as the work proceeds, and current totals of each item can be produced for each valuation. The method of recording re-measured work such as drainage on schedules will be found to be very useful for this purpose.

Clause 30 (2) states that the amount included in a valuation shall be the total amount of work properly executed subject to any agreement between the parties as to stage payments. Instead of using fixed periods of time for certificates the parties can agree to a certificate being issued at certain specific stages in the construction. This agreement would have to be worded very

*Example N: Stage Payment Chart*

## STAGE PAYMENT CHART

**Contract: 40 SEMI-DETACHED HOUSES WESTFORD**

| No. | Stage | Block Numbers 1 | 2 | 3 | 4 | 5 | 6 | 7 | 8 | 9 | 10 | 11 | 12 | 13 | 14 | 15 | 16 | 17 | 18 | 19 | 20 | Totals 1/8 | 1/9 | 1/10 |
|---|---|---|---|---|---|---|---|---|---|---|---|---|---|---|---|---|---|---|---|---|---|---|---|---|
| 1 | Ground Floor to First Floor | ✓ | ✓ | ✓ | ✓ | ✓ | ✓ | ✓ | ✓ | ✓ | | | ✓ | ✓ | | | | | | | | 4 | 7 | 11 |
| 2 | First Floor to wall plate | ✓ | ✓ | ✓ | ✓ | ✓ | ✓ | ✓ | | | | | | | | | | | | | | 3 | 4 | 7 |
| 3 | Topping Out | ✓ | ✓ | ✓ | ✓ | ✓ | | | | | | | | | | | | | | | | 2 | 3 | 5 |
| 4 | Roof Construction & Tiling | ✓ | ✓ | ✓ | ✓ | | | | | | | | | | | | | | | | | 2 | 3 | 4 |
| 5 | Plumber First Fix | ✓ | ✓ | ✓ | | | | | | | | | | | | | | | | | | 1 | 2 | 3 |
| 6 | Joiner First Fix | ✓ | ✓ | ✓ | ✓ | | | | | | | | | | | | | | | | | 1 | 2 | 4 |
| 7 | Plastering | ✓ | ✓ | | | | | | | | | | | | | | | | | | | 1 | 1 | 2 |
| 8 | Plumber Second Fix | ✓ | ✓ | | | | | | | | | | | | | | | | | | | — | 1 | 2 |
| 9 | Joiner Second Fix | ✓ | ✓ | | | | | | | | | | | | | | | | | | | — | — | 2 |
| 10 | Electrical | ✓ | | | | | | | | | | | | | | | | | | | | — | — | 1 |
| 11 | Painting External | ✓ | | | | | | | | | | | | | | | | | | | | — | — | 1 |
| 12 | Painting Internal | ✓ | | | | | | | | | | | | | | | | | | | | — | — | 1 |

*Example O: Stage Payments Statement*

*Contract:* 40 HOUSES WESTFORD                          *Valuation: No. 3*

*Contractor: L & L CONSTRUCTION LTD*                   *Date: 1/10/79*

| Stage No. | Stage Description | Total | Cost* | £ | p |
|---|---|---|---|---|---|
| 1 | Ground floor to first floor | 11 | £1520·00 | 16,720 | 00 |
| 2 | First floor to wall plate | 7 | £1650·00 | 11,550 | 00 |
| 3 | Topping out | 5 | £725·00 | 3,625 | 00 |
| 4 | Roof construction and tiling | 4 | £1080·00 | 4,320 | 00 |
| 5 | Plumber first fix | 3 | £350·00 | 1,050 | 00 |
| 6 | Joiner first fix | 4 | £920·00 | 3,680 | 00 |
| 7 | Plastering | 2 | £990·00 | 1,980 | 00 |
| 8 | Plumber second fix | 2 | £450·00 | 900 | 00 |
| 9 | Joiner second fix | 2 | £1030·00 | 2,060 | 00 |
| 10 | Electrical | 1 | £430·00 | 430 | 00 |
| 11 | Painter external | 1 | £250·00 | 250 | 00 |
| 12 | Painter internal | 1 | £300·00 | 300 | 00 |
| | | *Total to Valuation Summary* £ | | 46,865 | 00 |

*Sometimes percentages of the total cash values would be used.

carefully, so that the completion of each stage is clearly defined. Such clauses are usually inserted in the preliminaries bill, or in a special sheet incorporated with the contract documents.

On mass housing contracts it would be very exacting actually to measure the work in progress. The stage-payment basis, therefore, is invariably used, in which the construction of each unit is divided into anything from twelve to forty stages. A value for each stage is obtained from the contract bills, and charts are drawn up for all the units and stages; these are marked at each valuation at the completion of each stage. A condition is often made that a stage must be completed before any payment is made. A specimen chart for use in stage payments is given in Example N. These charts are used only for the repetitive part of the structure; substructure, drainage, siteworks, and other provisional sections of the contract bills are measured and included in valuations as the measurements progress. The totals of each stage are entered in the totals column with cash values attached, as shown in Example O. If the charts are completed with different colours for each valuation they will also record progress, and can be used for checking when certain sections of the work are completed. The valuation numbers could be used instead of ticks on Example N.

The value of prime cost and provisional sums are extracted from the contract bills before the allocation of stages is made. The work covered by these sums is included in a separate section of the valuation as goods supplied by nominated suppliers and work done by nominated sub-contractors.

### Variations

Variations should be included in valuations as part of the total value of work executed (see Clause 11 (5)). The contractor is entitled to payment on account in respect of variations, and this shows the importance of measuring and pricing variations at an early date. If the net total of variations is an omission it would be deducted instead of being added to the total amount of work as per contract.

### Nominated suppliers

Nominated suppliers' accounts must be included in interim valuations, and a statement of checked suppliers' accounts should be included with the valuation documents. These accounts should be totalled and the contractor's profit added in accordance with the amounts inserted in the contract bills. The sum total of these items should be brought into the valuation summary in the appropriate place, omitting the relevant prime cost and provisional sums. When issuing certificates to a contractor it is necessary for the architect to inform nominated sub-contractors of the amount included therein for them and direct the Contractor accordingly (Clause 27(b)); the reason for this is that nominated sub-contractors have the special privilege of being paid direct by the employer if the contractor defaults (Clause 27(c)). Many architects issue a similar notice to nominated suppliers also. Clause 28 (b) states that all nominated suppliers are declared to be 'suppliers to the contractor' but it appears that, apart from the nomination, they occupy just the same position as ordinary suppliers of materials to the contractor.

### Nominated sub-contractors

Nominated sub-contractors' accounts must be included in interim valuations. They should be checked and a statement of them should be included with the valuation documents (see Clause 27 (b)). These accounts should be totalled, and the contractor's profit added in accordance with the amounts inserted in the contract bills. The sum total of nominated sub-contractors' accounts should be brought into the valuation summary in the appropriate place, with the relevant provisional sums omitted.

The nominated sub-contractors' accounts for interim valuations will be forwarded to the surveyor by the contractor. These accounts should be carefully vetted and site measurements taken where necessary to verify the quantities stated. It may well be necessary to check the valuation with a consultant. The accounts often includes work executed to date as per quotation, extra works, materials on site, and perhaps fluctuations, all of which should be carefully checked. Some surveyors prefer to extract materials on site and fluctuations, and present these items under headings in the appropriate section together with the main contractor's claims. It is better, however, to keep the nominated sub-contractor's claim complete in the valuation, since the final statement for nominated sub-contractors, including extra work and fluctuations, will be kept separate in the final account. It only causes confusion, therefore, to split these accounts in interim valuations.

Clause 27 (b) states that the sums directed by the architect to be paid to nominated sub-contractors, less retention and discount, shall be paid by the contractor within fourteen days of receiving from the architect a certificate which includes the value of the work. This appears to mean that if the period of honouring certificates exceeded fourteen days, then the contractor would have to pay the sub-contractor before he received the money from the employer.

Clause 27(c) states that if the contractor should default in the payment of a nominated sub-contractor's account which has been included in a previous certificate, then the employer has the right to pay such accounts direct and deduct the amount from other sums payable to the contractor. This apparently, could be done only when the next certificate is due. It makes it essential, however, for the surveyor to see receipted accounts for any previous payments made to the contractor for nominated sub-contractors' accounts when he prepares an interim valuation.

Nominated sub-contractors often finish their duties in the early stages of the contract; for example, if they are employed on piling work. When this happens retention might be held on such a sub-contractor until the final release of retention. A provision is therefore made in the contract in Clause 27 (e) that if the architect wishes to secure final payment to a nominated sub-contractor before final payment is due to the main contractor, then he may include in a certificate an amount to cover the final payment to the nominated sub-contractor, and the retention money for the contract will be reduced in proportion. This can be done if the sub-contractor has indemnified the main contractor against any latent defects, and, with the exception of such defects, the contractor shall be discharged from all liability for the work of the nominated sub-contractor.

### Materials on site or adjacent to the Works

Contractors often expend large sums of money for materials which have to lie on the site, waiting to be used. If provisions for payments on account were confined to work executed, contractors would not receive payments on account for these materials until they were incorporated into the structure. To help reduce the contractor's financial load, provision is usually made for payments on account to include materials on site or adjacent to the Works.

This provision for the payment for materials on site is contained in Clause 30 (2) of the JCT form of contract, where it is stated that the amount due shall include the total value of materials and goods delivered upon the site for use in the works, up to and including a date of not more than seven days before the date of the certificate. This is provided that the materials are reasonably and not prematurely brought upon the site, and then only if adequately stored and protected against the weather and other risks. The amount so included for materials on site is to be subject to the retention stated in the Appendix.

The surveyor need not count materials on the site when he is preparing a valuation. Instead, he can check and approve a list of materials which has been prepared by the site agent, making sure that the claim appears reasonable and that no material is listed that would appear to have been prematurely brought upon the site. After this he need only tour the site with the agent to see the materials, and to make sure they are adequately stored and protected. The surveyor should value the materials from the basic-price list where possible; otherwise he can use current market prices or the actual invoices from the contractor. On large contracts the clerk of works could be briefed as to the exact conditions applicable to materials on site, so that he can agree a list with the site agent, ready for the surveyor's visit.

Clause 14 of the JCT form of contract states that materials which have been paid for in a certificate become the property of the employer. The contractor must not remove such materials from the site unless the architect has authorized this in writing, but he nevertheless remains responsible for any loss or damage to them.

Clause 30 (2A) in the JCT form of contract sets out complex conditions for the payment of materials which are not actually on site or adjacent to the works, but such payment is always at the discretion of the architect. Full compliance with these conditions is difficult to achieve in practice and when the possible liquidation of the contractor or supplier is contemplated, it would seem that payment must be considered very carefully. There is no provision in GC/Works/1 contract for payment for materials that are not actually on site.

The JCT form (1957 Edition), which was specially adapted for Local Authorities, often caused confusion when used for valuation for interim certificates which included materials on site. The parties to the contract had to insert a percentage in the Appendix, where there was a special provision, 'percentage of value of materials and goods to be certified'. In interim valuations materials on site were valued and were multiplied by these percentages, and the reduced amount was entered on the valuation summary. This entry should have been made below the provision for the deduction of retention, as the percentage reduction acted in lieu of retention. The advantage of this provision was that Local Authorities could if they wished keep a retention on materials on site which was higher than the retention for work executed. It will be seen that if the retention on work executed was 10%, and the percentage of materials and goods to be certified 80%, a retention of 20% was, in fact, being held on materials on site. The 1963 Edition has simplified this procedure by making the provisions for materials on site the same as for private work although some Local Authorities continue to unilaterally incorporate higher percentages for retention on unfixed materials.

### Retention

On building contracts it has long been the custom that payments on account should not be made in full. This is to enable the employer to retain some money actually due to the contractor as an incentive for the contractor to complete his obligations quickly; it also provides some security for the employer, should the contractor default. Clause 30 (3) of the JCT form of contract deals with retention. Provision is made in the Appendix to the conditions for the parties to insert a percentage against the item 'percentage of certified value retained'. Once again the standard form of contract is flexible and allows the parties to agree on appropriate retention provisions. The standard form recommends that the percentage shall not exceed 5%, but these words can be struck out and a different percentage inserted if so desired.

In the 1957 Edition of JCT form, the retention fund was dealt with in Clause 24 (d) (A) and Clause 24 (d) (B) which gave three alternative provisions to the parties as to how the money should be dealt with. In the first place they could come to an agreement between themselves. Failing this, they selected one of the two printed alternatives and struck out the others when the contract was signed. Clause 24 (d) (A) provided that the amounts retained from time to time as they were retained should constitute a 'retention fund' which was to be paid into the bank named in the Appendix, into an account in the joint names of the employer and the contractor, on deposit, at interest, and the principal and interest was held upon trust for the employer as security for the due completion of the works, until such time as the works were practically completed. The words 'practically completed' were not used here in a colloquial sense, but meant the practical completion of the works. This term has often caused confusion, but was interpreted as the time when the works were finished, although there may have been small defects still to be remedied. The accepted interpretation of this term in the building trade is the time when the building is handed over to the employer ready for occupation, from which date the maintenance period begins.

Clause 24 (d) (A) went on to provide that if the contractor was free from any claim for liquidated damages for delay under Clause 17 one moiety or half of the retention fund, including interest accrued to date, should be released to the contractor. The other moiety or half being held in trust in the joint account until the issue of the architect's final certificate, whereupon the principal plus interest accrued was paid to the contractor. Finally, if the employer defaulted the principal and interest in the retention fund was held upon trust for the contractor, and was paid by the employer, or any person legally entitled to deal with it, to the contractor.

The alternative provision in Clause 24 (d) (B) was not quite so favourable to the contractor. Here the employer retained the money held and enjoyed any interest accrued, and upon the practical completion of the works paid to the contractor one moiety or half of the total amount retained, subject to any counter-claim that the employer may have had for liquidated damages for delay. The other moiety was paid by the employer to the contractor when the architect issued the final certificate.

In the 1963 Edition of the JCT form (Clause 30 (4)) there are no alternative provisions for the retention fund. The moneys retained are to be held by the employer. However, it is expressly stated that the employer's interest in the fund is to be fiduciary as trustee for the contractor, but without obligation to invest. The contractor's beneficial interest in the moneys is subject to the right of the employer to have recourse thereto from time to time for the payment of amounts which he is entitled under the contract to deduct from any sum due to the contractor. This means that if the employer should go bankrupt the sum held as retention is not paid into the liquidator's pool, with the contractor contesting for his money as an ordinary creditor.

In the 1963 Edition the question of practical completion is clarified, since the form of contract requires the architect to issue a formal certificate of 'practical completion'. This contains no reference to the payment of moneys due, but simply certifies that the works have reached the stage of practical completion on the date of issue, and that the 'defects liability period' begins from this date.

Clause 30 (4) (b) states that when this is issued the architect must issue a certificate for one moiety or half the total amount retained. Clause 15 (4) states that when all defects have been made good to the satisfaction of the architect he must issue a formal 'certificate of completion of making good defects'. Clause 30 (4) (c) states that on expiry of the 'defects liability period' or when the certificate of completion of making good defects is issued, whichever is the later, the architect must issue a certificate for the residue of the amount retained. Complications arise, however, when there is a necessity for the final account to be audited – in the case, for example, of a Local Authority. There will be delays in paying the balance outstanding and it would seem that a clause should be inserted in the tendering documents explaining that a nominal retention will be held back pending audit.

### Fluctuations
In the JCT form of contract there is now an explicit provision for fluctuation claims to be included in interim certificates. The amounts due under Clause 31A or B are added to those certified in the interim certificates. If Clause 31F is not used and 31E does not include a percentage adjustment, it would seem that fluctuations can be included in an interim certificate without retention applied, provided that the claims have been checked and agreed.

### Penultimate certificates
The certificate issued at the practical completion of the works mentioned in Clause 30 (4) (b) is often referred to as the penultimate certificate. It has been argued that after the issue of a penultimate certificate the architect may not issue any further certificates until the final certificate is due. However, the words 'penultimate certificate' do not appear in the JCT form of contract, and

so there are no grounds for this argument. The architect can therefore issue such further certificates for payment as may be justified by the circumstances between the certificate issued on practical completion and the final certificate.

### Final certificate

Final certificates are dealt with under Clause 30 (6) and 30 (7), which states that on the expiration of the 'defects liability period' or upon the completion of the making good of defects, whichever is the later, the architect shall issue a final certificate. Such final certificates state:

(1) The contract sum adjusted as necessary in accordance with the terms of the contract
(2) The total amount paid to date to the contractor in interim certificates, and the release of retention
(3) The difference between these two amounts expressed as the debt due to or to be paid by the contractor.

Prior to the 1976 Revision of the JCT Form, Clause 30 (7) went on to state that unless notice of a dispute has been given before the final certificate has been issued the final certificate shall be conclusive evidence that the works have been properly carried out and completed, and that the work has been properly measured and valued in accordance with the terms of the contract. The final certificate shall be final and binding unless any sum mentioned in the certificate is erroneous for any of the following reasons:

(1) Fraud, dishonesty, or fraudulent concealment relating to the works
(2) Any defects, including omission of work, which a reasonable inspection or examination, at any reasonable time during the execution of the works or before the issue of the final certificate, would have disclosed
(3) Accidental inclusion of work or materials which would be incorrect, or any mathematical error in computations.

In the 1976 Revision, the wording of Clause 30 (7) was altered, possibly as a result of the Sutcliffe *v*. Thackrah case. Final certificates are *not* now conclusive as regards workmanship or materials except where work has been expressly required to be done to the reasonable satisfaction of the architect. It is for this reason that Clause 1 (1) has also been altered.

Undoubtedly the pre-1976 Clause 30 (7) gave the contractor many advantages. The condition that defects must be obvious to any reasonable inspection at any reasonable time left the employer exposed to a contractor's defence that the defects were obvious during the contract. The architect, on the other hand, could have found himself answering an action from the employer for negligence due to poor supervision, should the employer lose his action against the contractor. Moreover, this clause virtually signed away the employer's rights in law to bring an action against the contractor arising out of the contract after the final certificate has been issued. The employer can now bring an action at any time up to six years if the contract were under hand,

and up to twelve years if the contract were under seal, under the Limitation Act.

## GC/Works/1 form

### *Period of interim certificates*

Under this form of contract, certificates and advances on account are dealt with in Conditions 40, 41, and 42. The GC/Works/1 form of contract differs from the JCT form over the period of interim certificates. Condition 40 (3) states: 'The contractor may at intervals of not less than one month submit claims for payments of advances on account of work done and of things for incorporation.' From this it is obvious that although the period of interim certificates cannot be shorter than a month, there appears to be no upward limit; in practice, however, the monthly period is generally the rule.

A special provision is made in the second paragraph of Condition 40 (3) for contracts exceeding £100,000 in value. In such contracts the contractor is to be entitled to an advance on account at the end of every second week in the monthly period. This advance is an approximate estimate only, and is subject to the superintending officer's decision, which is final and conclusive.

Under this condition the contractor submits the claim for payment in both the fortnightly and the monthly claims (although the first is only an approximate estimate), supported by a valuation of the work done and materials delivered. The superintending officer certifies the sum to which the contractor is entitled.

Condition 42, as in the JCT form of contract, states that no interim certificate shall of itself be conclusive evidence that any work or materials are in accordance with the contract.

### *Work executed and variations*

The content of a valuation under the GC/Works/1 form of contract is very similar to that under the JCT form; the value of work done is to be valued at bills of quantities or schedule rates in the case of contracts without quantities. If the rates in the bills of quantities or schedule of rates are not applicable then the work should be valued on the basis set out in Condition 9. It will be seen from this that variations are intended to be included in interim valuations.

### *Nominated or selected sub-contractors and suppliers*

Condition 40 (6) states that nominated or selected sub-contractors' and suppliers' accounts shall be included in interim valuations. The provisions of the JCT form as to evidence of payment of nominated sub-contractors' accounts included in previous certificates are extended in the GC/Works/1 form of contract to nominated or selected suppliers. If requested by the superintending officer, the contractor is to supply evidence that all the accounts of sub-contractors and suppliers included in previous certificates have been discharged. Although the words 'nominated or selected' are not used, this may be understood, since only nominated or selected sub-contractors and suppliers could have been covered by any previous payments. This does not extend to the contractor's approved sub-contractors and suppliers. If the contractor defaults, the employing authority may recover the amount from the contractor (presumably from moneys due). In addition the employing authority may withhold any subsequent advance in whole or in part until such an account has been discharged by the contractor.

It should be noted that the superintending officer and the employing authority have two distinct and different duties under this clause. The superintending officer to decide whether or not the account or part thereof has been or has not been discharged. The employing authority to decide the amount to be recoverable or to be withheld. The decisions of the superintending officer and the employing authority to be final and conclusive and the authority can overrule the superintending officer.

In the GC/Works/1 form there is not such a strict time limit for the payment of nominated or selected sub-contractors' and suppliers' accounts; they need only be paid before the next certificate is issued. On contracts based upon monthly advances the contractor could presumably pay at any time within the month, but on contracts of over £100,000 in value Condition 40 (6) implies that such accounts should normally be paid within two weeks.

There is provision in Clause 40 (6) (b) for the Authority to pay the sub-contractor or supplier direct, but no provision for securing early final payments as in the JCT form.

### Materials on site
Materials on site are included in advances on account when they are reasonably brought on to the site and are adequately stored and protected (Clause 40 (2)). However, whereas under the JCT form materials paid for in interim certificates become the property of the employer, under the GC/Works/1 form Condition 3 they become the property of the employing authority immediately they are deposited on the site. There is no mention of change of ownership upon payment and it is interesting to note that not only materials but plant, temporary buildings and equipment, and anything else brought on to the site, become the property of the employing authority, and cannot be removed from the site without the superintending officer's written consent. The responsibility for safeguarding the materials on site still lies with the contractor, however.

### Retention
On this point the GC/Works/1 form is rigid, and there is no provision for the parties to agree their own terms as under the JCT form. Condition 40 (1) states that 97% of the value of work executed will be allowed in advances on account and the authority shall accumulate the balance as a reserve. Like the JCT form, the materials on site are included in advances on account, but at

97% of their value. The accumulated reserve lies in the hands of the employing authority alone, until the time when it should be released under the contract (see Condition 40 (1)).

Upon the practical completion of the contract, as defined in Condition 41, one-half of the accumulated reserve is released to the contractor, but the employing authority may after this date release further sums in reduction of the reserve 'as it thinks fit' (see Condition 41 (1)). If after the end of the maintenance period the superintending officer has certified the work as satisfactory, and if the final sum has been agreed, then:

(1) if the final sum exceeds the total amount paid to the contractor, the excess shall be paid to the contractor by the authority
(2) if the total amount paid to the contractor exceeds the final sum, the excess shall be paid to the authority by the contractor.

If the final sum is agreed before the end of the maintenance period, then:

(1) if the balance of the sum due to the contractor exceeds any reserve which the authority is for the time being entitled to retain, the excess shall be paid forthwith to the contractor by the authority
(2) if the total amount paid to the contractor exceeds the final sum, the excess shall be paid forthwith by the contractor to the authority.

### Final certificate

Final certificates under this form of contract are similar to final certificates under the JCT form, but it is not expressly stated what is the actual effect of the final certificate.

# 8. Tendering procedure

## Open tendering

This method is often used by Local Authorities to obtain tenders for building work. The employer advertises in the national and technical Press an open invitation to contractors to apply to the employer or his architect for the necessary documents, and gives brief details of the proposed works. One of the conditions in the advertisement is sometimes that the tenderer must pay a deposit which will be returned by the employer on receipt of a *bona fide* tender. This provision is made to deter persons applying for documents out of mere curiosity.

It is usually stated in the advertisement, and always in the tender documents, that the employer does not bind himself to accept the lowest or any tender. This advertisement does not legally bind the employer in any way, but is merely an invitation to persons to make an offer; this is necessary because an offer must be unconditionally accepted before a contract can be made.

Indiscriminate requests to tender of this nature are generally unprofitable, since they often lead to poor-quality building; and the preparation of such tenders throws upon the industry an unnecessary burden of time, effort, and expense. Contractors can be awarded work under this system which they are ill-equipped to carry out, financially and practically. Although the defence may be made that no special tender need be accepted, a committee spending public money is naturally tempted to accept the lowest offer.

## Selective tendering

Under this method competitive tenders are obtained by drawing up a short list of contractors and inviting them to submit a quotation. This short list can be drawn up in two ways. Either the employer's professional advisers name suitable contractors, or an advertisement is put in the national and technical Press, which sets out brief details of the proposed scheme and requests contractors who wish to be considered for inclusion in the short list to apply. The object of the selection is to make a list of firms, any one of which could be entrusted with the contract; after this the contractor chosen will simply be the one who submits the lowest tender.

The size of the short list may be limited to the small number of firms who satisfy all the requirements. When this is not possible the procedure laid down in the 1977 Edition of the Code of Procedure for Single Stage Selective Tendering should be followed.

## Negotiated contracts

This method of tendering is usually used for building work of a very difficult nature, where the magnitude of the contract may be unknown at first, or where early completion is most important. Under a contract of this nature there is usually no time to wait for drawings and bills of quantities to be prepared. There is always the danger that a price obtained in this way might be higher than against competition: however, intelligent use of a negotiated price may even result in a lower price.

Jobs with difficult phasing programmes are the obvious cases where a negotiated price should be considered, but it has other uses. By negotiating contracts it is possible to retain the services of firms which have been found satisfactory in the past.

Another method of selection is the serial system, which can result in very keen prices. Here selected contractors are invited to tender for one building – a school, for example – on the basis that the successful tenderer will be asked to build several other schools at the same rates. Naturally this encourages keener prices than for a single school, since the contractor will be able to organize his men and materials on the basis of an expected programme, and carry out this work more efficiently. Furthermore, experience gained on the earlier jobs will be useful later on, so long as the contracts are basically similar. This system of obtaining tenders has many advantages for the architects and quantity surveyors, since they are able accurately to estimate the cost of other jobs well in advance, on the basis of the known rates.

Although the serial type of negotiated tender can be based upon accurate bills of quantities, many negotiated contracts are arranged on a prime cost basis, with one contractor. There are three types of prime-cost contract in current use – the cost plus, cost plus fixed fee, and target cost with fluctuating fee.

### Cost plus contracts

In the cost plus contract the total cost of the works is recorded, and the tendered or negotiated plusages are added to give the total cost. The contractor would agree to undertake the execution of the works on the basis of the repayment by the employer of the total amounts of the following items:

(1) The actual cost of wages, fares, and allowances paid by the contractor to foreman, workmen, and staff (other than off site office staff) in respect of

such time as they are wholly employed upon the works, together with the amounts paid in respect of such wages for National Insurance, Graduated Pensions, Holidays with Pay Employer's Contributions, Employer's Liability, Workmen's Compensation Insurance and bonus payments previously authorized. With the addition of an agreed percentage.

(2) The actual cost of materials used upon the works after the deduction of all trade, cash, and other discounts and rebates exceeding 5%. With the addition of an agreed percentage.

(3) The actual cost of any sub-contractors' accounts in connection with the works, and any payments made on behalf of the employer. With the addition of an agreed percentage.

(4) The actual cost of any mechanical plant, consumable stores and services. With the addition of an agreed percentage.

Example P, part 1, shows how a typical final account for this type of contract would be prepared.

### Cost plus fixed fee

The total cost is also recorded with this system, and the fixed fee tendered or negotiated is added to give the total cost. The form of tender used for this type of contract would be very similar to the cost plus form, with a space provided where the fixed fee can be inserted in place of the various percentages. The fee is quoted in pounds, but it will be seen that a fairly accurate estimate of cost will be required for the contractor to arrive at the value of the fee. Therefore, this estimate of cost is usually calculated by the contractor.

Example P, part 2, shows a typical final account for this type of contract.

### Target cost with variable fee

The total cost is again recorded and compared with the target cost, which is usually calculated and agreed by both parties. The form of tender used would be very similar to the cost plus fixed fee form, but additional provision is made for the increase or decrease of the fee, should the final cost be below or above the target cost. The variable element is usually entered as a percentage of the net under- or over-expenditure. In Example P, parts 3 and 4, the figure of 20% has been inserted as the variable element. Note that this is 20% of the under- or over-expenditure and not 20% of the fee.

It is best to use this type of contract when a reasonably accurate estimate of the cost can be made, since it provides an incentive for the contractor to keep costs down in order to increase his fee. The fixed fee is not quite so satisfactory, as there is very little incentive to economize; the cost plus type of contract is the least satisfactory method, since the greater the cost, the higher will be the contractor's additions. A standard form of Contract for Cost plus contracts is now issued by the Joint Contracts Tribunal which defines in detail the basis of the prime cost.

*Example P: Specimen Final Accounts for Negotiated Contracts*

| | | £ | p | £ | p |
|---|---|---|---|---|---|
| 1. | *Cost Plus Contract* | | | | |
| | Labour cost | 40,000 | 00 | | |
| | Plus – say – 25% | 10,000 | 00 | 50,000 | 00 |
| | Materials cost | 60,000 | 00 | | |
| | Plus – say – 10% | 6,000 | 00 | 66,000 | 00 |
| | Sub-contractors' accounts | 10,000 | 00 | | |
| | Plus – say – 5% | 500 | 00 | 10,500 | 00 |
| | Mechanical plant, etc. | 2,000 | 00 | | |
| | Plus – say – 10% | 200 | 00 | 2,200 | 00 |
| | *Final Account* | | | £128,700 | 00 |
| 2. | *Cost Plus Fixed Fee Contract* | | | | |
| | Labour cost | 39,000 | 00 | | |
| | Materials cost | 59,000 | 00 | | |
| | Sub-contractors' accounts | 10,000 | 00 | | |
| | Mechanical plant | 2,000 | 00 | 110,00 | 00 |
| | Add fixed fee | | | 15,000 | 00 |
| | *Final Account* | | | £125,000 | 00 |
| 3. | *Target Cost with Variable Fee* | | | | |
| | (Target £110,000.00) | | | | |
| | Labour cost | 38,000 | 00 | | |
| | Materials cost | 58,000 | 00 | | |
| | Sub-contractors' accounts | 10,000 | 00 | | |
| | Mechanical plant, etc. | 2,000 | 00 | 108,000 | 00 |
| | Fee negotiated | 15,000 | 00 | | |
| | Plus 20% of £2000.00 | 400 | 00 | 15,400 | 00 |
| | *Final Account* | | | £123,400 | 00 |
| 4. | *Target Cost with Variable Fee* | | | | |
| | (Target £110,000.00) | | | | |
| | Labour cost | 41,000 | 00 | | |
| | Materials cost | 58,000 | 00 | | |
| | Sub-contractors' accounts | 10,000 | 00 | | |
| | Mechanical plant | 2,000 | 00 | 111,000 | 00 |
| | Fee negotiated | 15,000 | 00 | | |
| | Less 20% of £1000.00 over expenditure | 200 | 00 | 14,800 | 00 |
| | *Final Account* | | | £125,800 | 00 |

**The all-in service**

The system of the all-in service is becoming increasingly popular. It is very different from the more traditional method of building contracting, where the employer retains independent architects, quantity surveyors, and consultants to prepare a complete scheme for his project, and to protect his interests in negotiations with contractors. This method has been imported from the United States of America, where it has been accepted for the past hundred years or so. Ironically, there is a small but increasing tendency in the United States of America to use independent architects, quantity surveyors, and consultants. One reason for the introduction of the all-in service in this country has been the recent development of proprietary buildings by contracting organizations, who submit an all-in price for the erection of their particular building.

Under the all-in service the employer prepares a brief of his requirements, sometimes with professional advice; open or selective tenders are based upon this brief and the contractors prepare their own drawings, specifications, quantities, and prices. Each tenderer submits a scheme for his solution of the problem posed, complete with drawings, specifications, and a lump-sum price. This method appears at first to have several advantages for the employer, such as no direct professional fees, a fixed price, firm completion date, and so on, but it also has some disadvantages. The employer is, in fact, paying for the cost of previous unsuccessful tenders, which must be included in the overhead charges of the contract, he does not have the advantages of seeing the design evolve, he gets no approximate estimates, none of the advantages of professional advice, and usually he has to pay very heavily for any subsequent variations he may make. Nevertheless, the system is used more and more, and some of the all-in service organizations are going to great lengths to capture the market. In America firms even erect 'mock-ups' of the proposed buildings, which show many different types of construction and finishings from which the employer can choose before he enters into a contract. Such developments provide formidable competition, and professional architects and quantity surveyors must overhaul their existing service with particular view to cost control if they are to contest this tendency.

**Invitations to tender**

Each firm on the selected short list should be asked whether it is willing to tender, and should answer within a stipulated time, so that if necessary the reserve firms may be called upon. This invitation should be sent by the architect and should contain the following information:

(a) The names of the building owner, the architect, the quantity surveyor, and any consultants with supervisory duties
(b) Details of the form of contract to be used

*Example Q: Specimen letter of invitation to tender*

Dear Sirs,

I am authorized to invite you to submit a tender for the construction of the works described below. Your acceptance will imply your agreement to submit a wholly *bona fide* tender, and not to divulge your tender price to any person or body before the time for the submission of tenders.

If you are able to accept this invitation please inform me whether you will require any additional unbound copies of the Bills, or sections of the Bills of Quantities in addition to the one bound and one unbound copy that it is proposed to send you. These additional copies will be supplied on repayment of the costs of reproduction.

You are requested to send your answer by............................ Your inability to accept will in no way prejudice your opportunities for tendering for further work under my direction. In this connection your attention is drawn to Appendix A of the Code of Procedure for Single Stage Selective Tendering 1977 issued by the National Joint Consultative Committee for Building.

Yours faithfully,

.................................................... Architect

| | | |
|---|---|---|
| (a) | Job | .................................................................... |
| (b) | Employer | .................................................................... |
| (c) | Architect | .................................................................... |
| (d) | Quantity Surveyor | .................................................................... |
| (e) | Consultants | .................................................................... |
| (f) | Location of site | .................................................................... |
| (g) | Description of the works | .................................................................... |
| (h) | Approximate cost range | .................................................................... |
| (i) | Nominated sub-contractors | .................................................................... |
| (j) | Form of contract | .................................................................... |
| (k) | Percentage for Clause 31(E) | .................................................................... |
| (l) | Examination of priced bills (Alternative 1 or 2) | .................................................................... |
| (m) | The contract is to be under seal/under hand | .................................................................... |
| (n) | Date for possession | .................................................................... |
| (o) | Period of completion | .................................................................... |
| (p) | Date for dispatch of all tender documents | .................................................................... |
| (q) | Tender period | .................................................................... |
| (r) | Tender to remain open for .... weeks | .................................................................... |
| (s) | Liquidated damages | .................................................................... |
| (t) | Bond | .................................................................... |
| (u) | Particular conditions | .................................................................... |

(c) The location of the site
(d) A general description of the works, and a sufficient outline of the method of construction to enable tenderers to assess the character and size of the contract
(e) The proposed starting date of the contract. If time is to be the essence of the contract this should be made clear to the tenderers. The time for completion should be stipulated, and not made the subject of competition
(f) The proposed dates for the dispatch of the bills of quantities and submission of tenders
(g) A provision that acceptance of an invitation to tender is to bind the tenderer not to disclose his tender to any person or body before the time for the receipt of tenders
(h) A request that each tenderer should state how many unbound copies of the bills of quantities would be required in addition to the two copies it is proposed to send
(i) The latest date for the acceptance of the invitation.

Example Q shows a typical specimen letter of invitation to tender.

### Tender documents

The tender documents should be dispatched on the date stated in the invitation to tender. They should contain the following:

(1) Two copies of the complete bills of quantities, together with any additional copies or sections which may have been requested
(2) Prints of general arrangement drawings, sufficient to indicate the character, shape, and disposition of the works (see S M M Clause A5)
(3) Two copies of the Form of Tender
(4) One addressed envelope for the return of the Form of Tender, with an endorsement naming the contract
(5) Instructions for the return of the tender
(6) If the tender is based upon a contract with a fluctuations clause, the date on which basic prices are to be determined. This date should be some days before the date for the submission, in order to avoid hurried last-minute alterations. On contracts based upon the J C T form, a date ten days before the date for the delivery of tenders is given.

### Form of tender

The form of tender should be sent in duplicate, so that the tenderers can retain a copy of their offers. It should contain the following conditions:

(a) That the tenderer is willing to execute a form of agreement as described in the bills of quantities
(b) That any errors on the tenderer's part in the priced bills of quantities do

*Example R: Specimen Form of Tender*

---

## FORM OF TENDER

Tender for (description of works) ...........................................................................

To (Building Owner) .........................................................................................

Sir(s)

      I/We having read the Conditions of Contract and Bills of Quantities delivered to me/us and having examined the drawings referred to therein do hereby offer to execute and complete the whole of the works described for the sum of

...................................................................................... (£    :  )

and within the period stated in the Bills of Quantities* and I/we undertake in the event of your acceptance to execute with you a form of contract embodying all the conditions and terms contained in this offer.

      I/We agree that should palpable errors in pricing or errors in arithmetic be discovered before acceptance of this offer in the priced Bills of Quantities submitted by me/us that these errors be adjusted in accordance with the recommendations contained in paragraph 6 of the Code of Tendering Procedure currently published by the Joint Consultative Committee for Building.

To be
deleted
if not
applicable

      A list of Basic Prices of Materials and Goods on which this tender is based is attached to the Bills of Quantities and this list shall be used for the purpose of calculating the costs of Fluctuations in accordance with Clause 31 of the Conditions of Contract. The date on which the said Basic Prices were operative was .....................

      I/We further agree that this tender remains open for consideration for.................
weeks.

Dated this .......................................... day of .......................................................19.....

Name .................................................................................................................

Address .............................................................................................................

### Instructions to Tenderers

### (To be completed by the Architect)

Tenders are to be sealed in the endorsed envelope provided and delivered or sent by post to reach ......................................................................................................

..........................................................................................................................

not later than........... a.m. on...............     the...............     day of...............
19..........          p.m.

*Alternatively, the period for carrying out the works can be filled in by the competing contractors.

not affect the tender price, and that these errors will be adjusted in the manner described in the Code of Procedure for Single Stage Selective Tendering issued by the Joint Consultative Committee for Building (Paragraph 6).

Example R shows a specimen form of tender.

### Time for tendering

Except in special circumstances, four weeks should be allowed for the preparation of tenders. Shorter periods will seldom be enough to allow tenderers to obtain competitive estimates for the supply of materials or sub-contract quotations. The limit of the time of submission should be chosen so as to allow as short a time as possible to elapse before the opening of tenders. Any tender received after the specified time should not be considered.

### Cover prices

Very often contractors who are already hard-pressed by existing contracts are afraid to decline an offer to tender in case they prejudice the architect or employer against them for future work. They often therefore ask other contractors if they have been invited to tender, and, if they have, to give them a cover price, since they themselves are not interested in the contract. Usually a cover price is given at the last minute, and the tenderer completes his form of tender with this figure, and may submit it without even opening the bills of quantities.

This practice is bad, since it gives the employer the mistaken impression that all the tenders received are *bona fide*. This may be avoided if the invitations to tender make it clear that if the offer is declined this will not affect future invitations.

### Opening tenders

It is very important to notify tenderers quickly of the results of tenders, so that the unsuccessful contractors know that they are free to tender for other work. Also, the successful tenderer can then settle to the best advantage any sub-contracts and materials services. This should be considered a public duty. Each tenderer should be sent a complete list of the names and the amounts submitted by the other tenderers. It is recommended that the second lowest tender should be kept open until the lowest tenderer has been informed of the intention to accept his price and his priced bills of quantities have been examined.

The most convenient and quickest method of notification is to invite contractors to be present at the opening of tenders. They are usually invited to bring their tenders to the architect's office and in turn they each hand their quotations to the architect and employer. One drawback of this method is that it is not at all good for the nervous systems of the tenderers, especially if a low tender is opened first.

Conditional tenders are by far the greatest obstacle to equal tendering, and unfortunately these are made all too often. The problem can be dealt with by requiring that all proposed qualifications be submitted for approval during a predetermined time before the tender date. Any qualifications that were found to be satisfactory could then be circulated to all the tenderers as approved alternatives. This elimination of individual completion dates and qualifications would then make it possible to accept the tender in accordance with the Code of Procedure on Selective Tendering, recommended by the National Joint Consultative Committee for Building.

### Examination of priced bills of quantities

A letter of conditional acceptance is usually sent to the successful tenderer. This accepts his quotation, subject to entry into a formal contract as stated in the bills of quantities, and to the scrutiny of the contractor's priced bills of quantities. There is a good deal of difference of opinion as to whether priced bills of quantities should be submitted with tenders disclosed or undisclosed. Although there are arguments on both sides, such a course does involve the contractor in a great deal of extra time and expense, which is necessary only if his tender is accepted.

The examination of the priced bills of quantities should be made by the quantity surveyor, who should treat the document as strictly confidential; on no account should any details of the tenderer's pricing be disclosed to any person except the architect, unless the tenderer gives express permission. The first object of the examination is to detect any errors large enough to cause the tenderer to withdraw his tender. The quantity surveyor should report any such errors to the architect, who should inform the tenderer of their value and give him the opportunity of confirming or withdrawing his offer. If the tenderer withdraws, the priced bills of quantities of the second lowest tenderer should be examined.

When a tender is found to be free of serious errors, or if the tenderer confirms his offer in spite of the errors, the architect should inform the tenderer of the acceptance; before doing so, however, he would be well advised to obtain authority from the building owner. It is inadvisable to allow the tender to be altered, since various pieces of bad practice can occur, although this is sometimes done by the tenderer with the agreement of the other parties involved. It is most important that the priced bills of quantities should be checked before the contract is signed, since it is most difficult to rectify a written instrument when the mistake is discovered after the contract is made.

Any such errors should be adjusted by adding an endorsement to the priced bills of quantities, to indicate that all the rates or prices (excluding preliminary items, and prime cost and provisional sums) inserted therein by the tenderer are to be considered as reduced or increased in the same proportion as the corrected total of priced items exceeds or falls short of the original total of such items. This endorsement should be signed by both parties to the contract. Some surveyors, however, do not deduct the preliminary items as well as the prime cost and provisional sums before calculating the adjustment percentage. The argument for this is that the percentage adjustment should be made on the competitive element of the contract sum, the computation of which lies within the contractor's control. This, in fact, usually amounts to the contract sum less the amount of prime cost and provisional sums. On the other hand, the argument for the case of deducting preliminary items is that these items are usually priced as lump sums, which should not vary as long as the final account figure is in the region of the contract sum.

If the preliminaries are not deducted from the corrected total before the calculation of the adjustment percentage the result is that in the final account any variations that may occur will be subject to a lower percentage adjustment. This practice could also lead to a claim for the adjustment of lump-sum preliminary items in the final account, even if the variations were only minor.

Example S shows a typical corrected final summary, although the actual summary on the contract copy of the bills of quantities can be corrected, with the corrected summary and endorsement signed by both parties. Care should be taken that the alterations do not obscure the original figures: it is advisable to make corrections in red ink. If the corrections are extensive, however, a double-column cash sheet can be used, as in Example S. It should be signed by both parties to the contract, and inserted in the contract copy of the bills of quantities, with the original summary marked 'cancelled'.

It will be seen in Example S that the tenderer has rounded off his tender to £82,000.00, although the total of his calculations amounted to £82,056.30. The difference between these two sums amount to a rebate, which in this case is added to the errors since these are errors of under-calculation. If the rounding-off had been a surcharge the surcharge would have been deducted from the errors in the calculation of the adjustment percentage. In the final account for this contract all subsequent variations priced at bills of quantities rates, or at rates based thereon, will be subject to a reduction of 1.16%. All work measured and valued at bills of quantities rates and included in interim valuations will also be subject to a reduction of 1.16%.

To be correct, only the stipulated amounts of prime cost and provisional sums should be deducted before the adjustment percentage is calculated. This would leave under the contractor's control the amounts added for profit and attendance, within the net amount. It means, however, that the adjustment percentage would have to be applied to the amounts included for profit and

*Example S: Typical Corrected Final Summary*

### CORRECTED FINAL SUMMARY

| | Original £ | p | Corrected £ | p |
|---|---|---|---|---|
| Preliminaries | 11,260 | 00 | 11,260 | 00 |
| Excavation | 1,312 | 50 | 1,824 | 50 |
| Concrete work | 1,533 | 75 | 1,533 | 75 |
| Brickwork | 11,822 | 35 | 11,905 | 25 |
| Drainage | 1,355 | 25 | 1,355 | 25 |
| Roofing | 1,273 | 90 | 1,273 | 90 |
| Woodwork | 12,233 | 50 | 12,233 | 50 |
| Steelwork | 12,381 | 00 | 12,381 | 00 |
| Plumbing | 1,318 | 55 | 1,318 | 55 |
| Painting | 1,415 | 00 | 1,415 | 00 |
| External works | 11,555 | 50 | 11,565 | 50 |
| Prime cost and provisional sums | 14,595 | 00 | 14,595 | 00 |
| | 82,056 | 30 | 82,661 | 20 |

*Tender Figure Submitted: £82,000.00*

| | £ | p | £ | p |
|---|---|---|---|---|
| Corrected total | 82,661 | 20 | | |
| Original total | 82,056 | 30 | | |
| | | | 604 | 90 |
| Original total | 82,056 | 30 | | |
| Tender submitted | 82,000 | 00 | | |
| | | | 56 | 30 |

*Net Difference Between Corrected Tender and Tender Submitted*

£ 661 20

| | £ | p |
|---|---|---|
| Corrected total | 82,661 | 20 |
| *Less prime cost and provisional* sums and preliminaries | 25,855 | 00 |
| | £56,806 | 20 |

*Correction Factor*

Signed ........................

$$= \frac{661}{56\ 806} \times \frac{100}{1} = 1.16\% \text{ reduction or rebate}$$

Signed ........................

Date ........................

attendance on these sums in the final account, which would involve a laborious calculation. In practice, therefore, the amounts of prime cost and provisional sums, together with their profit and attendance items, are deducted entirely from the corrected total before the adjustment percentage is calculated.

The theory behind these percentage adjustments should be clearly understood. If the unit rates and calculations do not tally with the contract sum, then if there should be any variations it would be incorrect to value these at the rates contained in the bills of quantities. If the tenderer's errors amount to an under-computation, then the adjustment percentage is a reduction percentage; but it is an addition percentage if the tenderer's errors amount to an over-computation.

Although this method of adjusting errors in the pricing of bills of quantities for entire or lump-sum contracts by a percentage adjustment is theoretically correct, many surveyors consider it to be laborious and unnecessary – and sometimes even inequitable, particularly where approved sub-contractors are involved. A much simpler method of adjustment, which is often used when the errors are only slight, is to amend the errors by discussion and agreement with the contractor. This is done by adjusting other prices in the same trade, or alternatively by adjusting lump-sum items included in the preliminaries section of the bills of quantities. The best method of notifying tenderers of errors in bills of quantities is to schedule them on a list for easy reference, as shown in Example T: some surveyors set out the errors in a letter, but this is often very difficult to follow. The column in the schedule headed 'multiply by' is used when certain bills or sections are multiplied to arrive at the tender figure; for example, the bill for one garage is multiplied by sixteen on the summary for the sixteen garages in the contract.

When checking the tenderer's priced bills of quantities the surveyor should look for the correct transfer of totals to summaries and to the form of tender, as well as for arithmetical errors. Any items that are left unpriced should be recorded ready for notification to the contractor and if the tenderer does not intend to price them the rate column should be ticked, and short lines drawn through to the cash columns. Many contractors include minor labour items in the relevant unit prices instead of pricing them in actual labour items. In such cases the rate column should be ticked and the word 'included' written across the cash columns.

A further check should be made to see that similar rates are entered for similar items in different sections of the bills of quantities. This will ensure there is no disagreement as to which rate shall be used, should a variation occur on such items. The surveyor should also make sure that the rates inserted are reasonable and consistent. Although a particular tender may give the lowest total, inflated rates for certain variable items could make the final account higher than that of the second lowest tender. A surveyor, for example, who recommends the employer to enter into a contract on the basis of priced bills of quantities which contain a price of £50.00 a metre cube

*Example T: Schedule for recording errors in priced bills of quantities*

| Contract | | | | | | Observations on Priced Bills of Quantities submitted by Messrs. | | | | | | | | | |
|---|---|---|---|---|---|---|---|---|---|---|---|---|---|---|---|
| Bill No. | Page | Item | Now Reads | | Should Read | | Difference | | Multiply By | Add | | Deduct | | | |
| | | | £ | p | £ | p | £ | p | | £ | p | £ | p | | |
| | | | | | | | | | | | | | | | |
| | | | | | | | | | | | | | | | |
| | | | | | | | | | | | | | | | |
| | | | | | | | | | | | | | | | |
| | | | | | | | | | | | | | | | |
| | | | | | | | | | | | | | | | |
| | | | | | | | | | | | | | | | |
| | | | | | | | | | | | | | | | |
| | | | | | | | | | | | | | | | |
| | | | | | | | | | | | | | | | |
| | | | | | | | | | | | | | | | |
| | | | | | | | | | | | | | | | |
| | | | | | | | | | | | | | | | |
| | | | | | | | | | | | | | | | |

against a provisional item of extra for excavating through rock would clearly not be doing his duty. Some contractors give the impression of 'loading' certain prices in the bills of quantities at the expense of other items, with the risk that the 'loaded' items may be increased in the final account. The contractor should be asked to change such rates before the employer is advised to enter into a contract.

Care should be taken to see that all prime cost and provisional sums, as well as any contingency items, have been included in the tender. A contract signed with priced bills of quantities in which a contingency item of £1000.00 has not been priced out could be very difficult for the employer as well as the contractor. When the contractor knew that he had mistakenly made a gift to the employer of £1000.00 he would find every possible loophole in his efforts to regain the sum. Although the surveyor should check priced bills of quantities with very great thoroughness, the contractor remains responsible for his own errors in pricing or calculation (see Clause 13 of the JCT form).

Finally it should always be remembered that priced bills of quantities are checked for two reasons. The first is to see that the tenderer has not made such a serious mistake that he may prefer to withdraw his tender, which he may do at any time before unconditional acceptance. The second is to ensure that the rates can satisfactorily be used as a schedule of rates for the valuation of any subsequent variations, and to value work in progress for interim valuations.

Readers are referred to the 1977 Edition of the Code of Procedure for Selective Tendering, which provides information on the amendment of tenders to correct a genuine error.

# 9. Structure and organization of the building industry

At the time of writing there are approximately 80,000 firms engaged in the construction industry in England, Scotland and Wales. These fall into the following main groups:

General building
Building and civil engineering
Civil engineering contractors
Constructional engineers
Plumbing contractors
Joinery firms
Painting contractors
Roofing contractors
Plastering contractors
Glazing contractors
Demolition contractors
Scaffolding specialists
Reinforced concrete specialists
Heating and ventilating engineers
Electrical contractors
Asphalt and tar-spraying contractors
Plant-hire contractors
Flooring specialists
Insulating specialists
Suspended ceiling specialists
Floor and wall tiling specialists
Local Authorities' Works Departments

The 1976 Private Contractors' Construction Census and the 1976 Housing and Construction Statistics, both compiled by the DOE and published by HMSO in late 1977, show that there were about 83,000 firms plus Local Authorities' Works Departments, with an obvious steep decline in numbers evident since 1973. Private contractors employed 775,000 productive operatives, and 233,000 were employed by Local Authorities, etc. In addition, 246,000 administrative, professional, technical and clerical staff were employed by the private firms, and 114,000 by the Local Authorities' Works Departments. There was an estimated total of 1,678,000 persons

*Example U: The Structure of the Building Industry*

| | | | |
|---|---|---|---|
| THE STRUCTURE OF THE BUILDING INDUSTRY | | | |
| (Compiled from the 1976 Private Contractors' Construction Census and the 1976 Housing and Construction Statistics) | | | |
| *Number of work-people* | *Number of firms* | *Average value of work done per operative in third quarter of 1976 in £* | *Proportion of non-productive to productive workers* |
| 0–1 | 26,953 | 1,368 | — |
| 2–7 | 37,275 | 2,928 | 1–6.6 |
| 8–13 | 7,831 | 2,465 | 1–4.5 |
| 14–24 | 5,285 | 2,495 | 1–4.2 |
| 25–34 | 1,996 | 2,538 | 1–4 |
| 35–59 | 1,989 | 2,739 | 1–3.9 |
| 60–79 | 643 | 3,068 | 1–3.5 |
| 80–114 | 585 | 2,993 | 1–3.4 |
| 115–299 | 777 | 3,271 | 1–3.3 |
| 300–599 | 223 | 3,853 | 1–2.7 |
| 600–1199 | 119 | 3,750 | 1–2.5 |
| 1,200 and over | 63 | 3,659 | 1–3.2 |
| Approximate number of firms in the industry　= 83,700 | | | |
| Approximate annual turnover of the industry　= £13,000 million | | | |
| Total number of productive workers　= 1,008,000 | | | |
| Total number of persons employed, including working proprietors and welfare workers　= 1,678,000 | | | |

employed in the construction industry, including working proprietors and employees not covered by the census, and the value of work carried out was about £13,000 million per year.

It will be seen from the statistics set out in Example U that the industry is primarily composed of small firms. Of 83,000 firms engaged in the industry, approximately 77,000 employ under twenty-five persons. About 23% of the work done by general builders is carried out by these 77,000 firms and the nature of their work is mainly maintenance, small constructional work, and speculative housing. (In 1958, 45% of total work was carried out by firms employing less than twenty-five operatives.)

The figures for the work output per person employed show that the larger organizations achieved about 50% higher output than the smaller firms. The figures showing the proportion of non-productive to productive workers are very interesting, as they show that the firms with the ratio of 1 : 2.7 obtain the highest output. This refutes the theory that in the larger organizations there are too many non-productive workers.

To put these figures in a true perspective, it should be remembered that normally the larger firms make the maximum use of mechanical plant on larger contracts. Also, the nature of the work undertaken by many small firms does not give as great a scope for the use of mechanical plant. It would be interesting to know what the output per person would be if the larger firms were engaged in the type of work undertaken by the smaller units. There is no doubt, however, that the building industry will achieve increased productivity only as a result of increased mechanization and the use of more prefabricated components, with as little site labour as possible.

A large proportion of the manpower in the building industry is employed on remedial work, and there will always be a call for firms which specialize in this, since there is a vast amount of old property in this country. This is dealt with at present by many of the firms employing less than twenty-five persons. Housing development has absorbed a large proportion of the manpower in the building industry since the end of the war, in both Local Authority and speculative work. At the time of writing the output of housing units is in the region of 300,000 per year with a forecast dropping to 275,000 by 1979.

The construction industry has always been vulnerable to changes in government fiscal policies and there have been several notable peaks and troughs in recent years. In 1978 the industry was hoping that the bottom had at last been reached in the disastrous decline that started about 1973 and left a trail of liquidations and severe unemployment. Only time will tell whether good or harm will eventually come from this major recession.

**The operatives**

Building trade workers are organized into five unions:

Union of Construction, Allied Trades and Technicians (joiners, bricklayers, painters, masons, slaters and tilers, some labourers)
Transport and General Workers' Union (plasterers, Scottish slaters and tilers, scaffolders, steel-fixers, labourers)
General and Municipal Workers' Union (labourers)
Furniture, Timber and Allied Trades Union (woodcutting machinists)
Electrical, Electronic, Telecommunication and Plumbing Union (electricians and plumbers).

Building trade workers join these unions and usually pay a weekly contribution to them. The unions meet at local, regional and national level and are governed by elected committees; the day-to-day business is carried out by full-time union employees, who periodically visit contracts within their area.

Of the five unions listed above, the first four (UCATT, TGWU, GMWU and FTATU) are represented on the National Joint Council for the Building

Industry and the same, with the exception of the FTATU, are represented on the Civil Engineering Construction Conciliation Board. These two joint bodies negotiate and promulgate pay and conditions of employment for their respective sectors of the construction industry. National negotiations are also conducted in the Building and Civil Engineering Joint Board, a small body consisting of members of each side of the NJCBI and CECCB to whom those bodies delegate responsibility for discussing certain common matters, such as basic pay, the standard working week and holidays. Its decisions have to be reported back to the NJCBI and CECCB for formal adoption.

Pay and conditions for electricians and plumbers are fixed by Joint Industry Boards for their sectors of construction, and the EETPU is represented on these.

### The employers

Contractors are organized into the National Federation of Building Trades Employers. Other employers' associations in the industry are the Federation of Civil Engineering Contractors; the National Federation of Roofing Contractors; the National Association of Plumbing, Heating and Mechanical Services Contractors; and the Electrical Contractors' Association. The NFBTE and NFRC appoint the Employers' representatives on the NJCBI; the FCEC appoint the Employer's representatives on the CECCB. The NAPH & MSC and NFBTE appoint members of the Plumbing Joint Industry Board and the ECA appoints members of the Electrical Joint Industry Board. The NFBTE, largest of all these employers' associations, operates at local, regional and national level; it negotiates with the professions and Government departments at national level and acts on behalf of building contractors as a whole. This body also agrees rates of pay and conditions for road haulage workers in the building industry with the TGWU. The Federation of Master Builders also organizes building contractors, mainly smaller firms, but is not represented on the NJCBI.

### National Joint Council for the Building Industry

The NJCBI comprises, on the employers' side:

> National Federation of Building Trades Employers
> National Federation of Roofing Contractors

and, on the Operatives' side:

> Union of Construction, Allied Trades and Technicians
> Transport and General Workers' Union
> General and Municipal Workers' Union
> Furniture Timber and Allied Trades Union.

***Example V: National Joint Council***

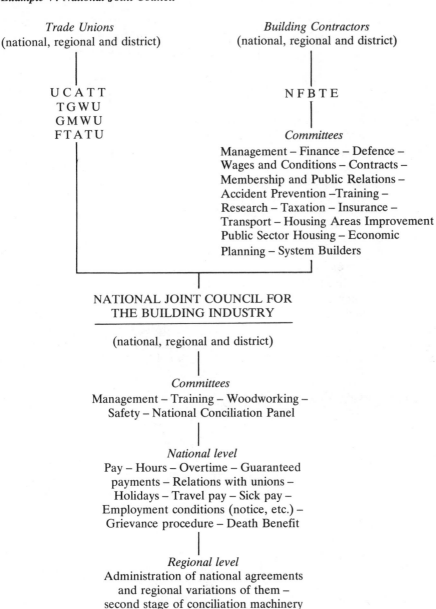

*Trade Unions*
(national, regional and district)

U C A T T
T G W U
G M W U
F T A T U

*Building Contractors*
(national, regional and district)

N F B T E

*Committees*
Management – Finance – Defence –
Wages and Conditions – Contracts –
Membership and Public Relations –
Accident Prevention –Training –
Research – Taxation – Insurance –
Transport – Housing Areas Improvement
Public Sector Housing – Economic
Planning – System Builders

NATIONAL JOINT COUNCIL FOR
THE BUILDING INDUSTRY

(national, regional and district)

*Committees*
Management – Training – Woodworking –
Safety – National Conciliation Panel

*National level*
Pay – Hours – Overtime – Guaranteed
payments – Relations with unions –
Holidays – Travel pay – Sick pay –
Employment conditions (notice, etc.) –
Grievance procedure – Death Benefit

*Regional level*
Administration of national agreements
and regional variations of them –
second stage of conciliation machinery

*Local or district level*
Administration of national agreements –
first stage of conciliation machinery

Its main functions are:

(1) The determination of wages and working conditions of building trades operatives through the National Working Rules for the Building Industry
(2) The settlement of grievances and disputes between employers and operatives
(3) The administration of the National Joint Training Scheme for skilled building occupations.

Regional Joint Committees of the NJCBI have in the past introduced 'regional amendments' to National Working Rules and those (all of which were introduced prior to January 1972) can be varied on application to the NJCBI. The ultimate power to amend lies at national level. Local Joint Committees are free to discuss the Working Rules but have no power to initiate or recommend variations to them. Their powers are confined to the administration and general supervision of the operation of the rules within their district.

### Prevention of disputes

The National Joint Council embodies in its Rules and Regulations a machinery whereby operatives, either individually or collectively, can process grievances or disputes. Under the machinery there is provision for reference of grievances to Local or Regional Joint Conciliation Panels. In emergency cases there is provision direct to Regional level and, in very special cases, a reference can be made direct to national level.

### National Working Rules

#### Wage rates

The National Joint Council fixes standard rates of pay for craftsmen, labourers and apprentices, and also rates for watchmen. Before October 1961 the country was graded into areas, with a variable wage rate for each area. Now, however, a national wage rate has been agreed; it operates everywhere except in London and Liverpool, where the wage rate is higher. Proportional wage rates have been agreed for apprentices and young male labourers, and these are set out in detail.

Rates of pay for watchmen are also agreed in this section; an amount per shift of either day or night duty. The 'plus rates' paid to trade charge hands appointed as such by the employer, over and above the standard rate for craftsmen, are agreed. Also included here are the rules laid down for rates payable to qualified benders and fixers of reinforcing bars, and qualified tubular scaffolders. The Annual and Public Holidays Agreement for operatives agreed by both sides of the industry is incorporated in Working Rule 1 (Wages) and both parties recognize in this rule the importance of suitable schemes of incentives.

*Working hours*

This section of the Working Rules lays down the weekly and daily working hours to be worked at plain time rates, with arrangements for meal intervals. Starting and finishing times in each area are to be determined and published by the local joint committee.

Working Rule 2A deals with time lost due to bad weather, etc. It prescribes that an operative shall, with qualifications, receive the guaranteed weekly minimum earnings laid down. The rule makes detailed provisions for the working of the above principles, and finally sets out the agreed procedure for the termination of employment by either the employer or the operative.

*Extra payments*

Provision is made here for additional payments to be made to operatives; these are divided into four sections, which are dealt with in detail under the following headings:

(a) Discomfort, inconvenience or risk
(b) Continuous extra skill or responsibility
(c) Intermittent responsibility
(d) Tool allowances paid to craftsmen and apprentices when in possession of a detailed prescribed list of tools
(e) Servicing of mechanical plant
(f) Storage of tools
(g) Clothing

*Overtime*

Under this section rules are set out for calculating the unproductive time paid to operatives who work above the normal working hours. Briefly, these provisions are as follows: time and a quarter for the first hour; time and a half for the next two hours; and double time thereafter until starting time the next morning. Time worked on Saturdays until 4 p.m. is paid at the rate of time and a half, and from 4 p.m. until normal starting time on Monday morning at double time. Rules are also laid down for operatives who work during holidays.

*Shift and night work*

Provision is made here for the payment of operatives who work at night and for men who work regularly in night gangs. For the regular night gangs special provisions are made for holidays, meal intervals, overtime, and so on.

*Travelling and lodging*

This rule sets out in great detail the provisions for the paying of travelling time and travelling expenses to men who have to travel from the employer's yard or office to their place of work. It also stipulates the agreed lodging allowances paid to operatives who have to live away from home in the course

## Example W: The structure of the building industry

of their work and the Inland Revenue's attitude towards income tax liabilities on these allowances.

### Supplementary rules for woodworking factories

The National Joint Council have agreed a supplementary set of rules for persons engaged in woodworking factories. Detailed provisions are made under the following headings:
(a) definition and scope
(b) rates of wages
(c) repetitive processes
(d) working hours
(e) overtime

### Health and welfare conditions

Both sides of the industry, through the machinery of the National Joint Council, have agreed to a national code of welfare (Construction [Health and Welfare] Regulations 1966 and Section 4 of the manual *Construction Safety*). Detailed provisions are made under the following headings:

(a) shelter from inclement weather
(b) protective clothing
(c) accommodation and provision of meals
(d) provision of drinking water
(e) sanitary conveniences
(f) washing facilities
(g) first aid
(h) site conditions

### National Joint Training Scheme for Skilled Building Occupations

The National Joint Council has instituted a scheme for encouraging and promoting apprenticeship within the industry. The apprenticeship is under the supervision of the local and regional joint apprenticeship committee, and this committee is party to the apprenticeship deed.

The boy learning a craft must be indentured under a National Standard Deed of Apprenticeship approved by the National Joint Council, and the prescribed period is to be three years.

### Agreements for holidays with pay

There are three separate agreements for holidays with pay: one to cover paid annual holiday, one to cover the winter holiday, and one to cover paid public holidays.

The Building and Civil Engineering Holiday Scheme Management Ltd is responsible for the administration of the annual holiday scheme. It is operated roughly on the principles of the National Insurance Acts, with every operative having a holiday credit card. These cards are the property of the employees but they are kept by the employer, who is responsible for the cards and the credit stamps affixed to them. In outline, the scheme is that the employer purchases stamps from the management company and fixes a stamp on the employee's card for every complete week worked in his service. When the holiday period begins the employer adds to the employee's pay packet the amount that he has in credit on the stamp cards, and forwards the cards to the management company, who reimburse the employer with the full amount paid.

This scheme has proved to be the only solution to the problem of holidays with pay for building trade workers, who by the very nature of the industry are itinerant employees. Under the scheme it is possible for an employer to pay out full holiday credits to an operative who may have been in his employment for only a week. The agreements have various detailed provisions to deal with most of the difficulties that can arise under this type of scheme. The amounts paid by employers under the scheme vary from time to time as the wage rates in the industry fluctuate, and the contributions are usually negotiated along with every wage agreement between both sides of the industry.

A similar credit stamp system used to be operated for the public holidays which fell outside the annual holidays, but it is now the normal practice for the employer to cover these and the winter holiday by making an allowance in the 'all-in' rates he uses in the compilation of his tenders.

## Organization of a building firm

Example X gives a graphic outline of a typical building firm employing about 600 work-people. There is no rigid pattern for the organization of such a firm; the plan usually evolves as the firm grows, and is adapted to suit the nature of the work it undertakes. For example, many of the larger building firms do not undertake any jobbing work at all, yet there are a few large organizations with flourishing jobbing-work sections which have grown proportionately with the firm from very small beginnings.

### Direction and policy

The direction and policy of the firm will be decided by the technical and managing directors. The managing director undertakes public relations work, contacts architects and prospective clients, deals with trade association work, and also with the development of general good-will. Some firms have one director specially for this work, and leave the day-to-day running of the business to another. In the organization shown in the example, the four persons in charge of construction, works management, estimating and surveying, and office management, have all been promoted within the firm, and are directors of the company. Including the managing director and the four technical directors, the firm employs thirty-nine non-productive persons.

*Example X: The Organization of a Building Firm Employing 600 Work-people*

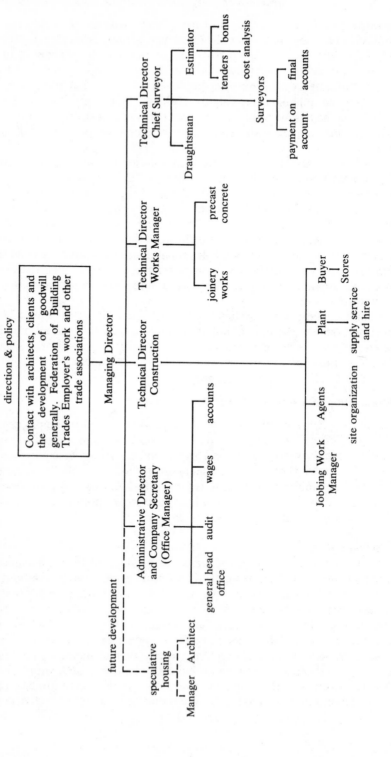

*Construction*

The construction work is supervised by the technical director, assisted by the senior agent. The duties are shared so that every contract in progress can be visited at least once a day. Six site agents are employed in this section, with one agent resident on each contract; if the work requires only the part-time services of an agent, one of the agents travels around two or three small contracts.

A jobbing manager and an assistant look after all jobbing work, visit the sites, supervise the labour, and requisition materials for this section.

The plant side of the business is dealt with by two fitters under a manager who arranges the transport of plant to the sites, and ensures that all plant is in working order. The plant manager is responsible for the organization of the increasing amount of hire work, and is also in charge of all the firm's lorries and all the lorry drivers.

The purchase of materials is dealt with by the firm's buyer, assisted by a typist. The buyer has a first-class knowledge of the local and national markets for materials, and pays particular attention to delivery dates and past records of delivery, in addition to competitive prices. A storeman is in charge of the stores at the yard, and many materials are held in stock, having been bought in bulk. The storeman is responsible to the buyer, who has instituted a rigid system of requisitioning for stores used from stock.

*Works management*

The firm has a small joinery works under a joinery shop manager and his assistant, where fifteen bench hands are employed. Most of the joinery required by the firm is made here, and a small amount of ready-made joinery sub-contract work is being developed. Two men are kept fully occupied making all the precast concrete work required for contracts; the joinery shop manager's assistant is responsible for the development of this side, apart from his duties in the joinery workshop. If further suitable workshop space could be found the firm could certainly run a flourishing joinery sub-contract section, and the directors are already looking for suitable accommodation for future expansion on this side.

Because of his special skill, the joinery manager is responsible for the buying of all timber, but all other materials are purchased by the buyer. The technical director in charge of the works, who has been a joiner by trade, visits most of the sites; he works in liaison with the site agents, as he holds the ultimate responsibility for the employment of all the firm's carpenters and joiners.

*Office management*

The general office of the firm is run by the office manager. Since he is a chartered accountant, he acts as company secretary, and is a director of the firm. Two men and a woman assistant work in the wages and salaries section of the office. Another person is employed full-time in the payment of accounts for materials and goods, and the rendering of accounts to clients. An assistant accountant with a woman assistant keeps all accountancy and cost records, and prepares an accurate monthly statement of the financial position of every contract. A pool of two typists and a comptometer operator provide all the typing and calculating services for the firm.

### Estimating and surveying

The chief surveyor is a director of the company, and is in charge of the preparation of all estimates, final accounts, interim payments, and bonus schemes. The estimator and his assistant prepare all tenders, draw up incentive schemes, and provide simple cost analysis data. The actual measuring of bonus work on site is carried out by four surveyors, who measure work in progress, prepare valuations for checking against monthly certificates, and agree the final accounts with the client's quantity surveyor. A draughtsman is kept busy preparing plans for small jobs, and for the expanding speculative housing side of the business.

### Future expansion

Within the past two years the firm has also entered into the field of good-class speculative housing. This side is doing very well, and there are plans for future developments. The company will require the full-time services of an imaginative architect for individual house design, and it is possible that this branch could expand into a separate section with a manager who would spend his time scouting for land, selling houses, and developing contacts for mortgage loans for prospective purchasers. Such a development would provide a constant demand for ready-made joinery, and thus help the proposed expansion of the joinery works.

### Builder's merchants

There are several thousand builders' merchants in the country who specialize in the sale of goods for builders and sub-contractors. Some merchants sell practically all the major materials supplied to the building trades, whereas others, such as plumbers' merchants and ironmongery suppliers, tend to specialize. Most of the major building materials, such as cement, bricks, aggregates, and steel, are obtained by contractors direct from the manufacturers, quarry owners, and steel stockholders.

As in many other forms of commerce, there is a complicated system of trade discounts on the sale of most goods. Instead of having as many as four separate prices for one article, the trade very often use the retail price alone in the preparation of price lists. Selling prices to the various sections of the trade are usually quoted at retail price, less a certain trade discount. The retail price of an article is the price charged to a private individual in a builders' merchant's shop. This price structure can be seen at work if you follow an article through the hands of the manufacturer, merchant, builder, and client;

the percentages used are not the exact figures quoted, but give a fairly accurate idea of the cost to a typical private citizen.

*Retail price*

(1)  The cost to manufacture the goods ........................................ less 50%
(2)  Manufacturer sells to merchant .............................................. less 40%
(3)  Merchant sells to builder ....................................................... less 20%
(4)  Builder sells to client ............................................................ retail price

This does not apply in the case of nominated suppliers, as already mentioned, since all trade discounts are to the advantage of the employer. The method of giving quotations as retail price less trade discount is still the basis of trading, although some merchants and suppliers prefer to quote a fixed figure. They may think this will conceal the existence of a resale price maintenance agreement in a few cases.

The trade discounts are not fixed on a standard basis; better discount facilities are available if the goods are bought in bulk. The amount of discount given is also affected by the volume of business as a whole over the year, and, not the least important, the speed at which bills are paid.

This system of trade discounts works out very fairly, although this is not immediately apparent. In return for his discount, the merchant saves the manufacturer the cost of maintaining a vast sales organization which would have to canvass each individual builder for business. Moreover, the merchant has large amounts of capital tied up in goods in stock, as well as having to pay overhead costs for storage. The builder earns his discount because he often buys in quantity, although very often in keen competitive tendering he gives away a large part of this discount in his efforts to secure the contract. Finally the competitive element keeps a firm check on the whole system of discounts throughout the trade.

## Manufacturers' trade associations

Some of the leading manufacturers of building materials have set up research and development organizations to carry out tests, and to give useful information and advice on the use of their products. Here is a list of some of the leading trade associations for building materials:

> Aluminium Window Federation
> British Electrical Association
> Cement and Concrete Association
> Copper Development Association
> Timber Research and Development Association
> Brick Development Association
> Gypsum Building Products Association
> National Federation of Clay Industries
> Rubber and Plastics Research Association
> Paint Research Association

### The Building Centre

This organization is supported by the various manufacturers of building materials. It has showrooms in London and several provincial centres where a large range of building materials is kept on permanent exhibition. The Centre acts as an agency from which the names of manufacturers, and their literature for any particular product, can be obtained.

### British Standards Institution

The British Standards Institution is a Government-sponsored body which sets up standard specifications for materials throughout the whole range of British industry. Any material that complies with the relevant British Standard specification is entitled to bear the Institution's 'kite' mark. Various committees have been established to frame these specifications, and those responsible for building materials include representatives of builders, architects and quantity surveyors, as well as experts in the manufacture of the materials concerned.

The Institution publishes standard specifications which can be obtained either singly or in groups arranged in handbooks, which are specially compiled to suit a particular industry. It also publishes British Standard Codes of Practice dealing with workmanship rather than materials, Drafts for Development and Published Documents.

### Agrément Board

The Agrément Board is an organization which assesses the fitness for use of new building and construction materials, components and systems. The assessments are published in Agrément Certificates. This body was set up in the United Kingdom in 1966 based on the French system.

The governing council of the board, which is appointed by the government, is made up of scientists, architects, engineers, and contractors, assisted by assessors from the British Standards Institution, Scottish Development Department, Department of the Environment, Greater London Council and the Building Research Station. The Agrément Board ties in its activities with the European Union of Agrément.

### Building Research Establishment

The Building Research Establishment (BRE) is a Government-financed group of laboratories carrying out research activities and serving all branches of the construction industry. It was founded in 1921 and was the first such organization in the world. In 1972 the Building Research Station merged with the Fire Research Station and the Princes Risborough Laboratory to form the present BRE. The laboratories are situated at Garston in Hertfordshire; Princes Risborough in Buckinghamshire and at East Kilbride, Glasgow.

**Building Advisory Service**

The Building Advisory Service was founded in 1954 and is an integral part of the National Federation of Building Trade Employers. Its function is to offer consultancy advice to the building industry on such subjects as financial planning and control, safety policies, etc., and to present various courses, conferences and seminars.

**Technical press**

The building industry is well served by the technical press, which in general represents fairly the points of view of all sides of the industry. In recent years an increasing number of the older journals have been bought out by publicity firms, who manage to issue them by post, free of charge, to *bona fide* members of the industry. This is because the revenue from advertising pays for the costs of production and distribution. It means, however, that the article content of such journals has to be reduced to an absolute minimum, since virtually all the space is given up to advertisements..

All the professional institutions issue regular journals to their members, and the standard of reporting in many of these journals has improved over recent years.

**Royal Institute of British Architects**

The Institute of British Architects was founded in 1834; the first Royal Charter was granted in 1837, and in 1866 by command of Queen Victoria the word Royal was incorporated in the title. The Institute first drew up a stringent code of professional conduct. Once this was firmly established it attended to the technical competence of members, and in 1863 instituted a voluntary examination system. In 1882 the Royal Institute was sufficiently established to be able to make the examinations compulsory for all candidates for admission to the Associate class membership. In 1902 students of certain recognized schools of architecture were exempted from the Institute's examinations, and in 1910 the RIBA Board of Architectural Education was created to take firm control of the training of architects.

At present the corporate membership of the Royal Institute of British Architects stands at about 28,000, with this number divided equally between those working in Local and Central Government posts and those working in a variety of private practices. The Royal Institute operates at branch level through the allied societies, which are generally grouped in regional offices. In these societies local architects discuss architectural affairs and on occasion send representatives to headquarters.

## Architects' Registration Council of the United Kingdom

At the turn of the century there were a number of practising architects who were not members of the RIBA, who had not passed any examinations, and who were not bound by the RIBA code of conduct. Only an Act of Parliament could prevent such people from entering the profession. After thirty years of hard work by the RIBA the two Architects' Registration Acts became law, in 1931 and 1938.

These Acts prevent any person from practising under the title of 'architect' unless his name appears on the National Register of Architects. Admission to the Register can now be obtained only by undergoing training and passing the examinations accepted for Associate Membership of the RIBA. Moreover, all registered architects are bound by a code of professional conduct based on, and identical in effect with, the RIBA code of conduct. Under the Acts a person who carries on a business under any style, name, or title containing the word 'architect' will be punished on summary conviction by a fine. The Registration Council has members appointed from many professional institutions and Government departments, and includes members appointed from the NFBTE, the NFBTO, and the RICS.

## Royal Institution of Chartered Surveyors

The Institution of Surveyors (a title that was later changed to the Surveyors Institution) was founded in 1863, with a membership of about 200. In 1881, when the membership had increased to about 500, a Royal Charter was granted by Queen Victoria. By 1918 there were about 5000 members, and four years later the Quantity Surveyors Association amalgamated with the Institution. The original name of the Institution was altered to the Chartered Surveyors Institution in 1930. The membership had increased to over 9000 by 1939, and in 1946 His Majesty King George VI, who was then Patron of the Institution, commanded that the Institution should in future be known as 'The Royal Institution of Chartered Surveyors'. At the moment the membership of the Royal Institution of Chartered Surveyors stands at over 46,000. The Institution is divided into the building surveyors' division, the general practice division, the land agency and agricultural division, the land surveyors' division, the minerals division, the planning and development division and the quantity surveyors' division. The quantity surveyors' division is the second largest, and through the quantity surveyors' divisional council the Institution takes a leading part in building affairs. The Institution operates at branch level throughout the country, with branches generally grouped on a county basis. The quantity surveyors' have their own divisional committee in most of the branches, which sends representatives to the quantity surveyors' divisional council at national level.

Membership of the Institution has for many years been limited to surveyors who have passed the Institution's examinations (first held in 1881). Surveyors who are either principals or assistants in private practice, officials in Central and Local Government departments, or who are engaged in teaching for the profession, may belong. Since 1967 surveyors who are employed in contractors' offices are eligible for membership.

## Institute of Quantity Surveyors

In comparison with other professional institutions, the Institute of Quantity Surveyors is comparatively young, having been founded in 1938 by a small group. The Institute has a very good system of examinations, which have been compulsory for entrants for many years. Membership is open to contractors' surveyors as well as to surveyors engaged in private practice and Central and Local Government departments. The Institute's membership has grown rapidly since the end of the Second World War, and currently stands at about 11,000.

Branches of the Institute are established in all parts of the British Isles and in many overseas countries. A monthly journal is issued which achieves a first-class coverage of quantity surveying affairs. A merger with the RICS was discussed for several years, but despite the majority of members of both bodies voting approval in 1976, the union did not take place because the IQS membership voting did not reach the required 75% majority.

## Institute of Building

The Institute of Building emerged from the Builders' Society formed by leading London master builders and was incorporated in 1884. At the present time the membership stands at over 25,000 and the Institute is active in the promotion of sound building practice and the stimulation of research. The members are engaged in building in a managerial, technical, scientific, commercial, educational or administrative capacity. The Institute structures its membership by means of the classification levels of technician, higher technician and professional, providing a 'ladder of opportunity' on satisfying the appropriate examination requirements. There are regional branches throughout the British Isles and in many overseas centres.

## National Joint Consultative Council of Architects, Quantity Surveyors, and Builders

This body was inaugurated in 1954 to co-ordinate a joint policy for the building industry on all matters that affect architects, quantity surveyors, and builders in the course of their professional work. The bodies represented on the committee are the National Federation of Building Trades Employers, the Royal Institute of British Architects, and the Royal Institution of Chartered Surveyors. The committee has discussed such topics as tendering procedure, fixed price contracts, and joint education and training, and publishes its findings in pamphlets. A Joint Consultative Committee has also been set up to deal exclusively with the affairs of interest to architects, quantity surveyors, and builders in London.

## Joint Contracts Tribunal

This body is composed of representatives from the National Federation of Building Trades Employers, the Royal Institute of British Architects, and the Royal Institution of Chartered Surveyors, together with several associations representing Local Authorities. The Tribunal is responsible for drawing up the standard forms of contract, and revising these documents periodically. From time to time it has issued 'Practice Notes' stating the opinion of the Tribunal on points of difficulty which have arisen in the interpretation of the forms of contract. These opinions greatly influence the day-to-day administration of the forms of contract, but have no legal force.

## Standard Method of Measurement Joint Committee

This committee was formed in 1922, when it produced the first Standard Method of Measurement of Building Work, in an effort to establish a uniform code of measurement throughout the country. The committee is composed of equal numbers of builders and quantity surveyors nominated by the National Federation of Building Trades Employers and the Royal Institution of Chartered Surveyors. Since 1922 this document has been revised six times, in the light of suggestions from all sides of the industry. In an effort to reduce the number of items in bills of quantities for small houses, the committee published a Code of Measurement for Small Dwellings just after the war, which is still used extensively. The Standard Method of Measurement is now so universally used that it is mentioned as the basis of measurement for preparing bills of quantities in both the J CT forms and the G C/Works/1 form of contract.

## Consultants

Some of the larger modern building contracts are so complex that the detailed design of certain parts are outside the scope of the architects. Consultants are therefore called in to prepare details of the particular aspect in which they are expert, and their fee is paid by the employer. Practically all the specialist construction firms employ their own design staffs, who are only too pleased to design a scheme for the architect, provided that their firm has the exclusive nomination. In these cases the cost of the design is included in the sub-contract tender figure. Some independent consultant firms employ specialist staff to cover all aspects of specialist services, thereby providing a comprehensive consultant service for the architect. Here is a list of such services, together with the particular specialist who would be concerned:

| | |
|---|---|
| Reinforced concrete and steel-framed structures | chartered civil engineers and structural engineers |
| Electrical installations | electrical engineering consultants |
| Heating and ventilating | heating and ventilating engineers |

# Appendix A: A summary of the JCT form of contract

Extracts reproduced by kind permission of RIBA Publications Limited.

Variants of the Standard Form are as follows: Local Authorities' Edition – with Quantities, without Quantities and with Approximate Quantities

Private Edition – with Quantities, without Quantities and with Approximate Quantities

## Private edition with quantities 1963 edition (July 1977 revision with amendments issued January 1978)

The Standard Form of Contract is basically divided into the following sections:

1) Articles of Agreement
2) Conditions of Contract
3) Appendix
4) Supplemental Agreement (The VAT Agreement)

### Articles of Agreement

These include a recital of the names of the employer, contractor, architect and quantity surveyor involved, the identification of the works, a schedule of drawings, the contract sum and provisions for witnessing signatures.

### Conditions of Contract

1   Contractor's obligations
2   Architect's instructions
3   Contract documents
4   Statutory obligations, notices fees and charges
5   Levels and setting out of the Works
6   Materials, goods and workmanship to conform to description, testing and inspection
7   Royalties and patent rights
8   Foreman-in-Charge
9   Access for Architect to the Works
10  Clerk of Works
11  Variations, provisional and prime cost sums
12  Contract bills
13  Contract sum
13A Value Added Tax – supplemental agreement

14   Materials and goods unfixed or off-site
15   Practical completion and defects liability
16   Partial possession by Employer
17   Assignment or sub-letting
18   Injury to persons and property and Employer's indemnity
19   Insurance against injury to persons and property
19A  Excepted risks – nuclear perils, etc.
20   Insurance of the Works against fire, etc.
21   Possession completion and postponement
22   Damages for non-completion
23   Extension of time
24   Loss and expense caused by disturbance of regular progress of the Works
25   Determination by Employer
26   Determination by Contractor
27   Nominated sub-contractors
28   Nominated suppliers
29   Artists and tradesmen
30   Certificates and payments
31   Fluctuations
32   Outbreak of hostilities
33   War damage
34   Antiquities
35   Arbitration

**Appendix**                                               Clause

Defects Liability Period [if none other      **15, 16** and **30** .........................................
stated is 6 months from the day
named in the Certificate of Practical
Completion of the Works].

Insurance cover for any one occurrence       **19**(1)(a) £....................
or series of occurrences arising out
of one event.

Percentage to cover Professional fees.       **20** [A].............................................

Date for Possession.                         **21** .................................................

Date for Completion.                         **21** .................................................

Liquidated and Ascertained Damages.          **22** at the rate of £            per................

*Period of delay:                            **26**
   (i) by reason of loss or damage           ................................................................
       caused by any one of the con-
       tingencies referred to in clause      ................................................................
       20[A]  or  clause  20[B]  (if
       applicable).                          ................................................................

                                             ................................................................

Clause

(ii) for any other reason.

............................................................................

Prime cost sums for which the    **27** (g) ..............................................
Contractor desires to tender.

............................................................................

............................................................................

Period of Interim Certificates [if none    **30** (1) ..............................................
stated is one month].

Retention Percentage (if less than five    **30** (3) ..............................................
per cent.).†

Period of Final Measurement and    **30** (5) ..............................................
Valuation [if none stated is 6
months from the day named in the
Certificate of Practical Completion
of the Works].

Percentage Additions    **31E** ..............................................

Formula Rules    **31F** (1)(a) (i)
    Rule 3:               Base Month.............................19..........
    Rules 10 and 30(i)       **Part I/Part II of Section 2 of the Formula
                                   Rules is to apply.

*Footnote.*—*It is suggested that the periods should be (i) three months and (ii) one month. It is essential that periods be inserted since otherwise no period of delay would be prescribed.*

†*Footnote.*—*The Percentage will be five per cent unless a lower rate is specified here.*

**Footnote.*—*Strike out according to which method of formula adjustment (Part I—Work Category Method or Part II—Work Group Method) has been notified in the Bills of Quantities issued to tenderers.*

**Supplemental Agreement** (The VAT Agreement)
1 Interim payments – addition of VAT – written assessment by Contractor, etc.
2 Value of supply – liquidated damages to be disregarded
3 Employer's right to challenge tax claimed by Contractor
4 Discharge of Employer from liability to pay tax to the Contractor
5 Awards by Arbitrator or Court
6 Arbitration provisions excluded
7 Employer's right where receipt not provided
8 Determination – additional tax

Amendment No. 15/1978
Issued January 1978

Amendments to the Standard Form of Building Contract 1963 edition (July 1977 Revision) Private and Local Authorities editions With and Without Quantities; and With Approximate Quantities (1975 edition as revised)

(The 1963 edition of the Standard Form With Quantities and Without Quantities was reprinted in April 1966, December 1967, July 1968, July 1969, July 1971, July 1972, July 1973, July 1975, July 1976, and July 1977 endorsed 'April 1966 revision', 'December 1967 issue', 'July 1968 revision', 'July 1969 revision', 'July 1971 revision', 'July 1972 revision', 'July 1973 revision', 'July 1975 revision', 'July 1976 revision', and 'July 1977 revision' respectively. The Standard Form With Approximate Quantities was first issued in October 1975 and is currently issued with Amendment Sheet AQ12/1976, Amendment Sheet No. 13/1976 and Amendment Sheet No. 14/1977.)

The details in Amendment No. 15 should be affixed to or within the cover of the Form of Agreement and initialled by the parties to the contract.

# Appendix B: JCT form of contract Practice Notes

These Practice Notes have been issued by the Joint Contracts Tribunal for the Standard Form of Building Contract. The Notes refer in each case to the Standard Form of Building Contract unless otherwise stated.

## Practice Note 1

Revised July 1971
*(Replaces Practice Note 1, published May 1964)*

### Clause 19(2)(a)—Insurances

1. When Clause 19(2)(a) was originally published in 1963 difficulties were encountered by users of the Standard Form and Practice Note 1 was issued in May 1964 after discussions with representatives of insurance interests to explain the intention of the Tribunal in drafting this Clause and to give advice upon how it should be operated in practice. Following the issue of the Practice Note the Tribunal discussed with the British Insurance Association whether any amendments to the text of the Clause were required. It was felt that amendments would assist users and in July 1968 a revised Clause was issued whose purpose was to set out the indemnity which the Employer required in terms which meant that that indemnity was normally insurable in the insurance market.

2. Users of the Standard Form are reminded that under Clause 18(2) the Contractor gives the Employer a full indemnity against all claims in respect of injury to any property which may arise from his negligence in carrying out the Works and under Clause 19(1)(b) the Contractor is obliged to cover that indemnity by such insurances as may be specifically required by the Contract Bills. Clause 19(2)(a) on the other hand provides for the insurance, for the Employer's benefit and protection as an owner or occupier of land, of loss or damage to adjoining property, whether his own or belonging to someone else, arising out of the carrying out of the Works but caused otherwise than by the negligence of the Contractor. In respect of this requirement of the Employer the Contractor has no other responsibility than to effect the insurance as instructed by the Architect.

3. In administering Clause 19(2)(a) the Architect or Quantity Surveyor on his behalf is required to do the following things:
   (1) Specifically to include in the Contract Bills the limit of indemnity for which the Contractor is to effect insurance for the Employer.
   (2) To include in the Contract Bills a provisional sum to cover that item.
   (3) After the contract is let, to issue instructions by virtue of Clause 11(3) in regard to the expenditure of the provisional sum.

4. The Clause calls for no action on the part of the Contractor at tender stage.

5. Clause 19(2)(a) now sets out the insurances which are to be maintained and it is important that Employers, Architects and Quantity Surveyors do not seek insurances in terms different from those now set out in the Clause.

6. It will be appreciated that the risks now referred to in the Clause, occurring without negligence on the part of the Contractor, arise mainly when the Works are close to existing buildings, must vary from job to job and will in a great number of cases be so remote as not to call for insurance.

7. Clause 19(2)(a), if insurance is required, calls for the inclusion of a provisional sum in the Contract Bills and it is for the Architect to decide from the nature of the proposed operations the amount of such sum to be included. Clearly where no insurance is required no provisional sum will be inserted. Where, however, there are risks which need to be covered by insurance then, after the Architect has consulted the Employer it is recommended that the Architect and Quantity Surveyor, as soon as possible after the contract is let, should meet the Contractor and, if possible, the Insurer's representative on site to examine all risks and agree the cover required. A quotation can then be given for the issue of a policy in the joint names of Employer and Contractor which the Architect can instruct the Contractor to accept.

July 1971

## Practice Note 2

Revised March 1975
(*Replaces Practice Note 2, published September 1964. Revised July 1971 and July 1973*)

### Clause 23(j) – Extensions of Time – Availability of labour, goods and materials.
1. Clause 23 (*j*) places a duty upon the Architect to grant the Contractor an extension of time where delay occurs by the Contractor's inability, for reasons beyond his control and which he could not reasonably have foreseen at the date of the Contract, to secure (i) such labour and/or (ii) such goods or materials as are essential to the proper carrying out of the Works. The sub-clause was divided into two paragraphs in July 1971 dealing separately with labour and materials.

2. A footnote to this sub-clause states that the parties are to strike out either the whole sub-clause or paragraph (i) or (ii) if their terms are not to apply.

3. In Clause 31F – Formula Adjustment – it is provided that Clause 23(*j*) and the remainder of Clause 23 as printed in the Standard Form must not be altered if the provisions of Clause 31F(7)(*a*) are to operate (i.e. restriction for adjustment during a period of default or alleged default over completion by the Contractor).

4. On Contracts where Clause 31F does not apply the deletion from the Conditions of either paragraph (i) or paragraph (ii) of Clause 23 (*j*) is a matter which requires very careful consideration at the tendering stage. Any deletion is a serious factor affecting the price and number of tenders submitted and should therefore only be considered where completion is of sufficient importance to the Employer to outweigh the additional cost of deleting the whole or part of the Clause. The extent to which the risk of shortage of labour or materials should be placed upon the Contractor must

therefore be considered on each tender in the light of the conditions prevailing at the time and architects should try to ensure that the materials and goods specified are available and likely to remain available for use in the contract.

5. The Clause should be deleted, whether in part or in whole, only if it is reasonable in all the relevant circumstances to expect contractors tendering for the work to take the risk of either labour or materials or both not being available.

March 1975

## Practice Note 3

### Clause 31 – Surcharge on Imported Materials
1. The Joint Contracts Tribunal has been asked to give guidance upon the position where materials or goods specified in a fixed price contract (i.e. where Clause 31\* does not form part of the contract) have become subject to the 15% surcharge.

2. The Tribunal cannot give guidance upon the legal interpretation of individual contracts. It is, however, of the opinion that this surcharge can only be treated in the same way as any other increase or decrease in the price of materials or labour not known at the date of the letting of the contract. Nevertheless, the Tribunal considers that whenever practicable the use of imported materials which will cause an increase in the cost of the Works should be avoided.

3. In the circumstances architects are reminded that they may after consultation with their clients and wherever it is feasible give sympathetic consideration to a variation of the specification to allow home produced goods to be substituted for those bearing import duty.

January 1965

*This Practice Note relates to clause 31 before the revision of the clause noted as B.(ii) in the List of Amendments, appended.*

## Practice Note 4

### Clause 31 – Fluctuations in Rates of Wages of Building Operatives
1. The Tribunal has been informed that in some cases doubt has arisen on the interpretation of Clause 31(1)(a)(i) as regards decisions of wage fixing bodies which are to come into effect on a date subsequent to the date of the decision of the wage fixing body.

2. It was the intention of the Tribunal that contractors when tendering should take into account for the purposes of Clause 31(1) all decisions of wage fixing bodies promulgated at the date of tender whether or not at the date of tender the actual wage changes etc. resulting from those decisions had been put into effect. In this respect Clause 31(6) provides as follows: 'The expression "the date of tender" as used in this condition means the date ten days before the date fixed for the receipt of tenders by the Employer'.

3. The Tribunal draws attention to the following words in Clause 31(1)(a)(i): 'The prices . . . contained in the Contract Bills are based upon the rates of wages and other

emoluments and expenses (including holiday credits) payable by the Contractor to workpeople . . . in accordance with the terms of the Building and Civil Engineering Annual and Public Holidays Agreements applicable to the Works and current at the date of tender'. It is the view of the Tribunal that the words, 'applicable to the Works and current at the date of tender' are directly referable to the 'rules or decisions of the (wage fixing body)'; such an interpretation is not only more natural but also gives effect to the intention of the Tribunal in drafting the clause as referred to above.

July 1965

## Practice Note 5

### Clause 31 – Timber used in Formwork

It is the opinion of the Tribunal that where a basic price for timber has been inserted in the list attached to the Contract Bill, adjustment for variation of cost should be made in respect of timber used in formwork. This opinion has been reached on the ground that timber used in formwork should be regarded as consumable stores and not by way of plant.* In ascertaining the amount of the adjustment account would be taken of the value of timber salvaged by the contractor. The Tribunal appreciated the difficulties which would arise if materials not incorporated in the work but used by way of plant were held to be subject to the fluctuation provisions.

July 1965

*Note definition of 'materials' in clause 31D(6)(b) of amended clause noted as B. (ii) in the List of Amendments, appended.*

## Practice Note 6

### Clause 28 – Nominated supplier – terms of contract – 5% cash discount

1. It is the opinion of the Tribunal that the Architect, before nominating a supplier to whom Clause 28 applies, is under a duty to satisfy himself that the supplier is prepared to furnish the Contractor with the materials or goods the subject of the P.C. sums upon the terms stated in that clause.

2. If a case should arise where a Nominated Supplier were unwilling to supply goods upon those terms, it was the duty of the Contractor to advise the Architect and seek his instructions before placing the order.*

3. There was no obligation upon the Employer to add the 5% cash discount to the cost of materials supplied by Nominated Suppliers unless the Architect varied the contract by instructing the Contractor to place his order with a Nominated Supplier who was unwilling to supply on the terms provided in Clause 28. Failure by the Contractor in such cases to seek the instructions of the Architect before placing his order with a Nominated Supplier might be held to constitute a waiver by the Contractor of his rights under Clause 28.

July 1965

*Clause 28 has been amended by the addition of paragraph (d), noted as F.(iv) in the List of Amendments, appended.*

## Practice Note 7

### Clauses 3 and 5 – Drawings—Additional Copies

With reference to the provisions of Clauses 3 and 5 of the Standard Form it is the opinion of the Tribunal that the Architect should supply to the Contractor such reasonable number of additional copies of drawings as he might require at the net cost of printing and despatch.

July 1965

## Practice Note 8

### Clause 30* – Certificates after issue of Certificate of Practical Completion

The Tribunal is aware that the certificate to be issued under Clause 30(4)(b) of the Standard Form of Contract is sometimes regarded as a penultimate certificate and therefore the Architect is precluded from issuing any further certificates until the final certificate becomes due under Clause 30(6). The Tribunal sees no grounds for construing the contract in this way and accordingly recommends that the Architect should issue such further certificates for payment as may be justified by the circumstances between the certificate issued under Clause 30(4)(b) and the final certificate.

July 1965

*This Practice Note relates to the clause before the amendment noted as F.(viii) on the List of Amendments, appended, which expressly provides for later Interim Certificates.*

## Practice Note 9

*This Note was withdrawn by the Joint Contracts Tribunal 31 October 1966.*

## Practice Note 10

Revised January 1975
*(Replaces Practice Note 10, published December 1965)*

### Clause 30(2A) and 14(2) – Payment for off-site materials and goods

1. In 1965 a new sub-clause (Clause 30(2A)) was published which gave a discretionary power to the Architect/Supervising Officer to include in Interim Certificates, subject to the conditions prescribed in the new sub-clause, the value of goods or materials intended for the works before their actual delivery to or adjacent to the Works. The previous provisions of Clause 30 merely provided in sub-clause (2) for the inclusion in interim payments of "materials and goods delivered to or adjacent to the Works for use thereon" together with certain qualifications set out later in sub-clause (2). Additional provisions were inserted in Clause 14 (a new sub-clause (2)) which stated that when payment for off-site goods and materials had been made by the Employer those goods and materials became the Employer's property but that the Contractor remained responsible for loss or damage thereto and for the cost of storage, handling and insurance. When the off-site goods and materials are delivered to or adjacent to the Works the provisions of Clause 14(1) in regard to responsibility by the Contractor become applicable.

2. Clause 30(2A) deals not only with off-site goods supplied by the Contractor himself but also those which are being obtained from suppliers or sub-contractors to the Contractor.

3. The reason for the inclusion of Clause 30(2A) was, subject to the safeguards set out in sub-clause (2A), to provide assistance to the cash flow problems of contractors and sub-contractors for off-site fabrication which is becoming an increasingly important part of building work. Earlier payment may assist the Employer in that the cost of financing off-site fabrication is reduced particularly if the decision to operate Clause 30(2A) is given to tenderers.

4. In contracts governed by Scots law it is not possible to apply the provisions of Clause 14(2) and 30(2A) (which have therefore been deleted in the Scottish Supplement to the Standard Form) because of differences between English and Scots law but alternative procedure (which enables the employer to pay for off-site materials and goods) is provided in the Scottish Supplement by an additional Clause 30(9) applicable only to contracts let under that Supplement. It is essential that the Employer enters into a separate contract with the Contractor and the Sub-Contractor or supplier as the case may be in order effectively to transfer the right of property in the materials and/or goods concerned. Copies of these contracts together with full instructions may be obtained from the Scottish Building Contract Committee, 15 Rutland Square, Edinburgh EH1 2BE.

5. While the operation of these provisions is a matter for the discretion of the Architect/Supervising Officer, the Tribunal considers that, particularly where goods are being specifically fabricated for the Works by or through the Main Contractor, the discretionary powers should be exercised wherever appropriate. Attention is, however, drawn to the importance of careful compliance with the terms of Clause 30(2A) and Clause 14(2) particularly in relation to identifying the off-site goods and materials which are being paid for by the Employer and their adequate insurance in respect of loss or damage.

January 1975

## Practice Note 11

**Clause 31 – Redundancy Payments Act 1965**
1. The Redundancy Payments Act 1965 established the redundancy fund which is financed by a surcharge on the employers' National Insurance contributions. The Tribunal confirms that contributions for such purposes collected through the machinery established under the National Insurance Acts are to be regarded as within the scope of Clause 31 of the 1963 Form of Contract. Nevertheless, the Tribunal considers that Clause 31(1)(b)(i) of the contract might not be apt to cover increases in the rate of employers' contribution under the National Insurance Acts where the increases are levied for such purposes.

2. The following amendments to Clause 31 have, therefore, been approved by the Tribunal:

**Private and Local Authorities Forms (with Quantities)**
(1) Clause 31(1)(b)(i) to read:
    'The prices contained in the Contract Bills are based upon the rates of employers'

compulsory contributions payable at the date of tender under or by virtue of any Act of Parliament.'

(2) Clause 31(1)(b)(ii), lines 1–4 to read:
'If any of the said rates of contribution be increased or decreased after the date of tender or if any new statutory contribution becomes payable after that date, then the net amount of the difference between what the Contractor actually pays in respect of workpeople engaged upon or in connection with the Works and what he would have paid in respect of such persons had any of the said rates not been altered or had a new contribution not become payable,'

### Private and Local Authorities Forms (without Quantities)

(1) Clause 31(1)(b)(i) to read:
'The rates contained in the Schedule of Rates are based upon the rates of employers' compulsory contributions payable at the date of tender under or by virtue of any Act of Parliament.'

(2) Clause 31(1)(b)(ii), lines 1–4 to read:
'If any of the said rate of contribution be increased or decreased after the date of tender or if any new statutory contribution becomes payable after that date, then the net amount of the difference between what the Contractor actually pays in respect of workpeople engaged upon or in connection with the Works and what he would have paid in respect of such persons had any of the said rates not been altered or had a new contribution not become payable,'

3. It would not be the Tribunal's view that the levy imposed by the Construction Industry Training Board under powers derived from the Industrial Training Act 1964, is an 'employers' contribution' within the meaning of the revisions to Clause 31 set out in this Practice Note.

4. The above amendments have been incorporated in all editions of the Standard Forms printed after 31 March 1966 and which bear the description '1963 Edition, Revised April 1966' on the back sheet.

April 1966

## Practice Note 12

### London Government Act 1939

Section 91 of the London Government Act, 1939, was repealed as from 1 April 1965 by Section 93(1) and Schedule 18 Part II of the London Government Act 1963. The employees of the Greater London Council and of the London boroughs are now subject to section 123 of the Local Government Act 1933 (Local Government Act 1965, Section 8(2)). Accordingly, Clause 25(3) of the two Local Authorities editions of the Standard Form need only refer to the Local Government Act of 1933* and reference to Section 91 of the London Government Act 1939 should be deleted from that clause.

The above amendments have been incorporated in all copies of the Local Authorities editions of the Standard Form printed after 31 March 1966 and which bear the description '1963 Edition, Revised April 1966' on the back sheet.

April 1966

*Re-enacted as S.123 of the Local Government Act 1972.*

## Practice Note 13

### Application in Scotland of Practice Notes 1–12

1. Following on the adoption in Scotland of the Standard Form of Building Contract in October 1965 it is thought desirable to issue a restatement of the Practice Notes issued by the Tribunal to date clarifying their effect in Scotland.

### Practice Note 1 – Clause 19(2)(a) Insurance

2. Although the wording of this clause in the Scottish Supplement differs from that in the 'Standard Form' Conditions, the advice given in this Practice Note still applies and should be followed in Scotland.

### Practice Note 2–8

3. The advice and comments contained in these Practice Notes apply equally in Scotland.

### Practice Note 9 – National Schedule of Daywork Charges

4. This Practice Note was withdrawn in October 1966 by the Tribunal and its withdrawal applies equally to Scotland.

### Practice Note 10 – Clause 30(2A) – Payment for off-site goods and materials

5. The discretionary power given to an architect by this clause (which appears in the April 1966 revision) to authorize payment to a contractor for off-site goods and materials cannot be exercised in Scotland without the exchange of a separate contract between the Employer and the Contractor. Clause 14(2) and Clause 30(2)(a) should therefore be deleted in all cases where the contract is applicable to building in Scotland.

6. The form of contract referred to above, together with full instructions as to when and how it should be used is obtainable from the Secretary, Scottish Building Contract Committee, 15 Rutland Square, Edinburgh.

### Practice Note 11 – Redundancy Payments Act 1965

7. The amendments to Clause 31 made by this Practice Note are included in the April 1966 revision and apply to Scotland. This has been adopted by the Scottish Building Contract Committee.

### Practice Note 12

8. This Practice Note refers to the repeal of certain Local Authority Acts which do not apply to Scotland and although included in the April 1966 revision to the 'Standard Form' Contract, do not form part of the Scottish Supplement.

April 1967


## Practice Note 14

### Changeover to Metric – Clause 11

1. Those responsible for the design specification and preparation of Bills of Quantities for building work are now (December 1963) taking into account the *Programme for the Change to the Metric System in the Construction Industry PD 6030* published by the *British Standards Institution* which has been charged with planning and co-ordinating

the changeover to metric in the construction industry. Under this programme key dates are as follows:

(a) 1 January 1969, when designers are expected to start designing new projects in metric terms.

(b) 1 January 1970, when contractors will be expected to start working to drawings and documents in metric terms for some new projects.

(c) 15 February 1971, when decimal currency will be introduced.

(d) 31 December 1972, by which time the bulk of the change to metric for contractors should have occurred.

(e) After December 1973, no new work should be in imperial terms.

2. In the early stages of the designer's changeover, i.e. during the early part of 1969, metric designs are likely to involve many existing imperial sized components and materials. As the changeover proceeds more and more metric sized components and materials will become available which will be incorporated progressively into metric designs. However, owing to the inevitable time lag between the design stage for a project, the contractor may find, when carrying out the work, that components and materials referred to in one measure in the contract documents are not in fact available in the measure or size.

3. If the situation envisaged in paragraph 2 above occurs on contracts let under the Tribunal's Standard Form it is suggested that the Contractor should, as soon as it is apparent that components and materials specified in imperial measure or size are not available, seek instructions from the Architect. The Contractor could not, it is suggested, substitute materials or goods in a measure or size other than that given in the contract documents without an Architect's instruction and moreover substitution of a different measure or size may have design implications which the Architect will obviously need to consider. The Architect's subsequent instructions, whether they are to substitute goods or materials in the only measure or size available or whether they involve in addition a re-design, constitute, in the Tribunal's view, a 'variation' and will thus fall to be valued under Clause 11.

4. It is to be hoped, however, that before a contract is entered into the parties will try to ensure that the contract documents take into account all available information as to the change-over to metric in the various supply industries and in this way keep to a minimum the number of variation instructions that have to be issued.

December 1968

## Practice Note 15

### Clause 31 – Fluctuations – Use of A or B – 'Firm price' – list of materials

1. The Tribunal published in October 1967 a revised Clause 31 – Fluctuations. The Clause is divided into four parts, A, B, C and D. Parts A and B are alternatives. Parts C and D are applicable whichever alternative is used. A contract should, therefore, contain either Parts A, C and D or Parts B, C and D.

2. Parts A, C and D are available for use where the parties have agreed to allow full fluctuations:

(i) on the cost (including the cost of any levy, contribution or tax) of employing workpeople engaged upon or in connection with the work; and

(ii) in the market price of materials as set out on the basic price-list attached to the Contract Bills.

3. Parts B, C and D should be used whenever the full fluctuation clause is not applicable. Part B is a limited fluctuation clause allowing for rises and falls in the cost of employing workpeople due to changes, not in wages, but in the contributions, levies and taxes payable by the contractor as a result of an Act of Parliament or Orders made thereunder, or due to new contributions, levies and taxes of this kind. Part B also allows for rises and falls not in the market price but in the amount of duty or taxes imposed on materials, specified (but not priced) in a list agreed by the parties as a result of an Act of Parliament or in Orders made thereunder.

4. The Tribunal has been advised that on occasions the whole of Clause 31 is being deleted. Whilst the Tribunal recognises that the parties may agree to deletions in the contract it wishes to emphasise that it intended Part B to be used in all cases where Part A was not applicable.

5. In regard to contracts in the public sector the Tribunal has noted the terms of paragraph 13 of the *Ministry of Housing and Local Government Circular 79/67 (Welsh Office 69/67)* that the Ministry will regard contracts as being firm price if they include Clause 31, Parts B, C and D. It is understood that the Scottish Development Office will shortly be issuing a circular containing advice similar to that contained in the above circulars. The Tribunal wishes to draw the attention of authorities in the public sector to these circulars.

6. The Tribunal has been notified that some building owners are insisting that materials on which at the date of tender there is no duty should not be placed on the list of materials envisaged in Part B. The Tribunal wishes it to be known that it had always intended that new duties should be within the scope of Part B and that materials upon which at the date of tender there was no duty payable could be included in the list.

April 1969

*Clause 31E has been added to Parts A, C and D or B, C and D by the amendment noted as G.(xv) in the List of Amendments, appended. Clause 31F has been added as a further alternative to Part A and Part B/C, D and E by the amendment noted as H.(i).*

## Practice Note 16

### Fixed Fee Form of Prime Cost Contract

1.1 The Joint Contracts Tribunal has considered queries that have been raised, in connection with the Fixed Fee Form of Prime Cost Contract, as to the difficulty of defining the circumstances in which an Architect's instructions alter "the nature or the scope of the Works" and which the Contractor, under clause 3 of the Form, is not obliged to carry out.

1.2 The Tribunal consider that disputes as to what instructions have this effect will not arise frequently and will be settled quickly to enable the work to proceed either by a further agreement awarding an additional Fee or by paying for the work that is outside the original nature or scope of the Works on a quantum meruit basis. Nevertheless the parties can help to avoid disputes arising by making sure when entering into a contract on the Form:

(a) that the Specification is as comprehensive as possible as to the nature and scope of the Works;
(b) that where the Specification cannot give sufficient information on parts of the Works, then those parts should be referred to by a Provisional Sum;
(c) that the estimate of Prime Cost agreed by the parties (on which the Fixed Fee is normally calculated) is realistic in relation to the information available when the contract is entered into.

1.3 Where Provisional Sums are used for works whose nature or scope cannot be adequately set out in the Specification then the Sums should be included in the estimate of Prime Cost recorded in the Third Schedule.

2.1 The Tribunal has also considered queries on the operation of Clause 7(1) of this Form which so far as relevant provides;

"The Contractor shall . . . provide all the labour, materials, goods, plant, stores and services required for the carrying out and completion of the Works: Provided that the Contractor shall not at any time make a greater provision than is reasonably required for the carrying out and completion of the Works in accordance with this Agreement and to the extent that any provision is unreasonable it shall be made by the Contractor at his own cost."

2.2 The Tribunal recommends that any disallowance of Prime Cost under the Proviso to Clause 7(1) should be made within a reasonable period after the alleged over-provision has occurred.

May 1969

## Practice Note 17

**Value Added Tax**
Issued in separate booklet

## Practice Note 18

**Formula Price Adjustment**
Issued in separate booklet (but see Practice Note 23)

## Practice Note 19

**Clauses 19, 19A, 20 and 30(2A) – Insurance Provisions**

**Clause 20[A](1) – Insurance for the 'Full Value'**
1. Clause 20[A](1) provides that all work executed and all unfixed materials and goods delivered to, placed on or adjacent to the Works are to be insured in the joint names of the Employer and the Contractor 'for the full value thereof (plus the percentage (if any) named in the Appendix to these Conditions to cover professional fees)'. It is important that sufficient insurance money is available, in the event of any of the perils referred to in clause 20[A] occurring, for the cost of reinstatement. If the insurance money is not sufficient for such reinstatement the shortfall would be the responsibility of the Contractor.

2. With the escalating cost of building work, regular reviews of the sum assured under clause 20[A] are essential. Consideration should also be given to obtaining policies in accordance with the obligations under clause 20[A] which provide for an uplift in the value of the sum insured by a percentage which will adequately reflect the cost of inflation in respect of building costs and professional fees.

*Note: The following paragraphs relate to the July 1975 Revision Amendments, noted as H.(iv)—(xi) and (xix) in List of Amendments, appended.*

### Public and Employer's Liability
3. **Clause 19(1)(a)** has been amended as at 1 July 1975 and no longer deals separately with the liability of contractors and sub-contractors for injury or death to persons and injury or damage to property. With the exception of Employer's Liability Policies which may be unlimited in amount no insurance policy for public liability is issued without a limit on the amount of indemnity being given for any one occurrence. The former subclause (1) (a) has been interpreted by certain users as placing upon the Contractor an obligation to obtain indemnity for third party liability for death or injury to persons for an unlimited amount for any one occurrence. As such cover was not available in the insurance market, the Tribunal has been advised that it would be desirable to provide for a limit of indemnity for all third party liability for any one occurrence to be stated in the contract documents. The revised sub-clause (1) (a) so provides for such limit to be stated in the Appendix. Such limit is a minimum requirement and it is appreciated that many Contractors may have a greater cover.

4. In regard to the amount of insurance cover this is a matter for individual Employers and Contractors to decide; but the British Insurance Association with whom this matter has been discussed advise that the indemnity for third party liability must be realistic and wherever necessary the advice of insurance experts on the amount of cover should be obtained.

5. In regard to the liability of the Contractor to his employees insurance is compulsory by statute upon employers and subclause 19(1) (a) therefore reminds them of the obligation on Contractors and Sub-Contractors to comply with the relevant legislation, the Employers' Liability (Compulsory Insurance) Act, 1969.

6. The Tribunal recommends Contractors and Sub-Contractors not to terminate their insurance cover in accordance with clause 19(1)(a) until at least the expiry of the Defects Liability Period. In no circumstances should such cover be terminated at the date of practical completion.

### Clause 20 and new clause 19A
7. (i) The risks to which Parts [A], [B] and [C] of clause 20 refer have been modified to deal with loss or damage arising from certain nuclear perils. The reason for this is that liability for such perils is placed by statute upon those engaged in nuclear activities and they are bound by statute to provide appropriate compensation. Insurance is available in respect of such risks only to those to whom the statute applies and not to Contractors. Clause 20[A] thus excludes from the risks for which insurance has to be taken out those nuclear perils; and the new clause, clause 19A, states that they are not perils for which the Contractor, his servants or agents, is liable to the Employer. Clause 20[B] (Local Authorities Edition) is similarly modified; and in the private Edition, which includes an insurance requirement on the Employer, exempts the

Employer from insuring for such perils. Similar changes to those for Part [B] in the Private Edition have been made to Part [C].

(ii) Similarly loss or damage from pressure waves caused by aircraft travelling at sonic or supersonic speeds has been excluded as insurance cover is not available against this peril.

(iii) The footnote, formerly referring solely to clause 20[C], now applies to clause 20[A], and, in the Private Edition, to the insurance obligations in clause 20[B]. The Tribunal have been informed that on occasions insurance against certain perils (e.g. riot and civil commotion) may not be obtainable.

### Clause 20[A] – Insurance cover on determination of employment of Contractor
8. Where a Contractor's employment is determined, whether under clause 25 or clause 26, Employers should consider whether under clause 20[A] the insurance taken out in the joint names is or is not being continued. A Contractor's insurance obligations under clause 20[A] are complied with either by a specific policy covering loss or damage from the risks referred to in clause 20[A]; or by endorsing the Employer's interest on the Contractor's annual policy.

9. Where a specific policy in the joint names is used this cannot be terminated by one party so that the Employer will not be put in the position of having his insurance cover discontinued without his knowledge. Where, however, a Contractor's annual policy is used the Contractor could unilaterally discontinue this policy and there would be no specific obligation on the insurer to inform the Employer of this; to protect themselves, Employers should in such cases request the insurer not to cancel cover without reference to the Employer. The likelihood of this ever occurring has been minimised by an amendment to clause 20[A] which makes clear that the 'Employer's interest' is in the Contractor's policy which was not made clear in the previous drafting.

### Clause 30(2A) – Off-site Goods and Materials – Insurance
10. Where clause 30(2A) is operated and the Employer has paid for off-site goods and materials, clause 14(2) provides that 'the Contractor shall nevertheless be responsible for any loss thereof or damage thereto and for the cost of storage handling and insurance of the same'. No requirement as to what, if any, insurance had to be provided was included. Clause 30(2A) has now been amended by the inclusion of an additional paragraph in the proviso – paragraph (i) – which sets out the various conditions etc. which have to be satisfied before clause 30(2A) can be operated. The new paragraph (i) means that satisfactory insurance cover for the contingencies referred to in clause 20 (that is loss or damage by fire, lightning, explosion etc.) must be provided so that clause 30(2A) can be operated. As the policies of insurance of the manufacturer could normally only cover goods or materials in his ownership, such policies would not apply to goods or materials stored with the manufacturer but which, under the provisions of clause 30(2A), are owned by the Employer. It will normally be necessary for insurance cover to be obtained against the contingencies referred to in the new paragraph (i) to clause 30(2A). The interests of both Contractor and Employer in any such insurance cover must be secured. This insurance cover does not include certain risks such as risks during transit or theft, and it is a matter for the Contractor to decide if he needs to take out such additional cover.

11. Once goods and materials to which clause 30(2A) applies are placed on, or adjacent to, the site of the Works the risk of loss or damage by the contingencies referred to in clause 20 will be dealt with under clause 20[A], 20[B] or 20[C] in accordance with whichever part of clause 20 is included in the contract for loss or damage to the Works and materials on site.

July 1975

## Practice Note 20

### Standard form of Building Contract for use with Bills of Approximate Quantities
*New form first issued October 1975 – Private and Local Authorities Editions — Adaptation of Standard Form WITH Quantities, 1963 edition (July 1975 revision)*

1. The Tribunal received representations that, judged by value, a considerable volume of work, particularly in the private sector, was let on the basis of Bills of Approximate Quantities so that the Works have to be completely re-measured. For such work the Standard Form for use 'WITH Quantities' is not suitable since it does not provide for general re-measurement of the work to be executed but only for adjustment of work executed as a result of Architect's instructions involving a variation or the expenditure of a provisional sum and the remeasurement of any sections of the quantities specifically marked as 'Provisional' in the Contract Bills. The Tribunal therefore decided, with the approval of its constituent bodies, that it would be desirable to issue an adaptation of the 'WITH Quantities' form to make it suitable for use where, at the tender stage, it is made clear to the Contractor that the quantities in the Bills are approximate and are all subject to re-measurement.

2. The Tribunal has now published two new forms of contract. The new forms are the 'Standard Form of Building Contract with APPROXIMATE Quantities Local Authorities Edition 1975 Issue' and 'Standard Form of Building Contract with APPROXIMATE Quantities Private Edition 1975 Issue'. The headnote to these forms states: 'This form is for use where the Works have been substantially designed but not completely detailed so that the quantities shown in the Bills are approximate and are subject to re-measurement.'

3. Although the Scottish Building Contract Committee had previously advised the Tribunal that there was not sufficient demand for such a Form in Scotland for them to issue a Scottish Supplement adapting the provisions of the Form to Scottish law the Committee is, at the date of issue of this Practice Note, reviewing the matter.

4. *There is appended to this Note a list of the differences between these new forms of contract and the Standard Form WITH Quantities 1963 Edition (July 1975 Revision) which should enable users to identify the changes that have been made. The following paragraphs of this Practice Note draw attention to the more important features of the two new forms and the circumstances in which the Tribunal intends them to be used.* References to 'the Form' are to both the Private and Local Authorities editions.

5. The *recitals* of the Articles of Agreement of the Form state that the Bills of Approximate Quantities describe the work to be done and are also 'intended to set out a reasonably accurate forecast of the quantity of the work to be done'. This important qualification is intended to prevent the use of this Form for Works which have not been substantially designed with the result that the quantities do not set out a

reasonably accurate forecast of the quantity of the Works. For the position where this intention is not fulfilled see both paragraph 11 below, where it refers to clause 13(3) (b), and new paragraph (m) in clause 23 (Extension of time).

6. The new Form should NOT be used where only certain sections of the quantities in the Bills are approximate (for example: abnormal foundations; drainage; external works). In such cases the Standard Form ('WITH Quantities') should be used and the relevant items in the Contract Bills marked 'Provisional'.

7. The *Articles* provide for the insertion of a 'Tender Price' which is the total of the prices inserted by the Contractor in the Bills of Approximate Quantities. This Tender Price will always be converted as a result of the provisions on re-measurement and valuation contained in the Contract Conditions and the total payment to be made to the Contractor is referred to throughout as the 'Ascertained Final Sum'.

8. *Clause 11*, entitled 'Contract Bills', deals with the priced Bills of Approximate Quantities which are defined in the Articles of Agreement as 'the Contract Bills'. These set out the quality and quantity of the work included in the 'Tender Price'. Since, however, that quantity is only approximate, the actual work carried out in accordance with the Contract Drawings and the Architect's/Supervising Officer's instructions will have to be re-measured. Such re-measurement is not a variation under this Contract since the quantity of work to be carried out has never been fixed and cannot therefore be subject to a variation. For this reason the definition of 'variation', which appears in Clause 12(2) of the new Form, omits any reference to a change in quantity.

9. *Clause 13(1)* provides for the measurement and valuation of all work (except work resulting from instructions as to the expenditure of prime cost sums for nominated sub-contractors and work for which a tender from the Contractor under Clause 27(g) is accepted).

10. *Clause 13(2)* provides that the re-measurement must be carried out using the same principles of measurement as have been used for the preparation of the Contract Bills.

11. *Clause 13(3)* contains the rules for the valuation of the measured work which follow those for variations in Clause 11(4) of the Standard Form ('WITH Quantities' and 'WITHOUT Quantities'). The main differences, however, are:
(i) Rule (b) has been expanded to provide for the situation where, contrary to the intention expressed in the Articles (see paragraph 5 above), the approximate quantities were *not* a reasonably accurate forecast of the quantity of the work. In these circumstances if the rates in the Contract Bills do not provide a reasonable basis the Contractor is entitled to be paid a 'fair valuation' of the actual quantity of the work he is instructed to carry out. *Work whose quantity is not reasonably accurately forecast is never valued under Rule (a).*
(ii) Rule (c) requires the Quantity Surveyor to take into account the effect of any percentage or lump sum adjustments priced in the Contract Bills in applying Rules (a) and (b) for valuation of the measured work.

12. The adjustment of the Preliminaries section of the Contract Bills is dealt with in Clause 30(5)(c)(vii) where it is specifically required that the Preliminaries shall be adjusted 'where appropriate' to take account of the valuation of the work measured by the Quantity Surveyor under Clause 13(3)(b). Thus where the re-measured work was

not reasonably accurately forecast or is not of similar character or is not executed under similar conditions as the work in the Contract Bills, the Quantity Surveyor must take into account the pricing of any Preliminary items related thereto, and, where appropriate, make the necessary adjustment to the Preliminaries in the calculation of the Ascertained Final Sum. If the Quantity Surveyor deals with the Preliminaries element in arriving at a fair valuation under Rule 13(3)(b) then no further adjustment would be required under Clause 30(5)(c) (vii).

13. *Clause 13(4)* deals with the valuation on a daywork basis of work which cannot properly be measured and valued by the Quantity Surveyor.

14. *Clause 13(5)* provides, like Clause 11(6) in the Standard Form ('WITH Quantities' and 'WITHOUT Quantities') for the ascertainment of any direct loss and/or expense as a result of the execution by the Contractor of a variation or of work for which a provisional sum has been included in the Contract Bills; and has also been extended to apply to work by the Contractor whose quantity was not reasonably accurately forecast in the Contract Bills. The clause has not been extended to apply to work covered by approximate quantities which were a reasonably accurate forecast of the quantity of the work actually carried out since the Rules in Clause 13(1) and (2) for valuing such work are considered to be adequate.

15. *Clause 23 (m)* is new and gives as ground for extension of time the execution of work the quantity of which was not reasonably accurately forecast in the Contract Bills.

16. *Clause 30(5)* deals with the computation of the Ascertained Final Sum:

*Paragraph (a)* requires the Contractor to send all the documents and accounts necessary for the computations to the Architect or Quantity Surveyor either before or within a reasonable time after Practical Completion.

These would not include the priced Bills of Remeasurement which *paragraph (b)* requires the Quantity Surveyor to supply to the Contractor not later than the end of the period of Final Measurement and Valuation stated in the Appendix.

*Paragraph (c)* defines in detail what must be included in the Ascertained Final Sum and is drafted on the assumption that the Quantity Surveyor 'starts with a blank sheet of paper' and builds up the Ascertained Final Sum in a logical and orderly way. The 10 sub-paragraphs of paragraph (c) should ensure that nothing which is appropriate in the Contract Bills is omitted from the Ascertained Final Sum.

The general 'sweeping-up' provisions in *sub-paragraph (x)* would include such items, where relevant, as:

| Clauses | | |
|---|---|---|
| 5 | Correction of setting out | (Deduction) |
| 6 | Testing | (Possible addition) |
| 7 | Patents/Royalties | (Possible addition) |
| 15(2)&(3) | Making Good Defects | (Deduction) |
| 19(1)(c) | | |
| 19(2)(c) | Default in insuring | (Deduction) |
| 20[A] | | |
| 24 | Claims for disturbance | (Addition) |
| 25 | Determination | (Deduction or addition) |

17. The new Form provides only for Clause 31A – Fluctuations and Clause 31F – Formula Adjustment. Clause 31B of the Standard Form 'WITH Quantities' is omitted (Clause 31B is used only with firm price contracts). Inasmuch as work under the 'APPROXIMATE Quantities' Form is not such that the Contractor can himself at an early stage obtain and place firm orders for the work a 'firm price' is inappropriate. Moreover such work would not be within the criteria for thorough pre-planning set out in the Department of the Environment Circular (Circular 85/72, Welsh Office 181/72, dated 18th September, 1972) entitled 'Tender and Contract Procedures for Building and Civil Engineering Work: Firm Price Tendering'. Contracts let under this Form in the public sector do not, therefore, have to be on a firm price and will thus include either Clause 31A or Clause 31F – Formula Adjustment.

18. Where *Clause 31F – Formula Adjustment* – is used the Formula Rules Parts I and III apply; Part II – Works Groups – is not to apply since the quantities, being approximate, would not be suitable for use in preparing the Work Group Indices which require the use of the tender weightings of the work in the various Work Categories.

**Appendix**
List of differences between the new Standard Form 'With APPROXIMATE Quantities' and the Standard Form 'WITH Quantities' 1963 Edition (July 1975 Revision)

*Heading*
The headnote applies only to this Form.

*Recitals and Articles*
The recitals refer to 'Bills of Approximate Quantities', and this phrase is used instead of 'Bills of Quantities' throughout the Form; refer to those Bills setting out 'a reasonably accurate forecast of the quantity' of the Work to be done; and refer to the totals of the prices in the Bills of Approximate Quantities as 'the Tender Price', and this phrase is used where relevant in place of 'Contract Sum'. Article 2 is new and refers to the final total sum to be paid to the Contractor as 'the Ascertained Final Sum'.

*Clause 1(2)*
The discrepancy or divergence is limited to that between the Contract Drawings and 'the description in' the Contracts Bills; divergence as to quantity is dealt with by remeasurement under Clause 13.

*Clause 4(2)*
The fees and charges are to be 'included in the calculation of the Ascertained Final Sum' except where paragraph (a) or (b) applies.

*Clause 5*
The second sentence has been re-drafted.

*Clause 6(3)*
The cost is to be 'included in the calculation of the Ascertained Final Sum'.

*Clause 7*
'Tender Price' for 'Contract Sum'. In Proviso royalties etc. are to be 'included in the calculation of the Ascertained Final Sum'.

*Clause 11*
Omitted. New Clause 11 entitled 'Contract Bills' follows, with necessary changes, Clause 12 of the Standard Form also entitled 'Contract Bills'.

*Clause 12*
Omitted. New Clause 12 follows, with necessary changes, Clause 11(1), (2) and (3) of the Standard Form. Clause 12(2) – definition of 'variation' – omits the reference to 'quantity': see Practice Note, paragraph 8.

*Clause 13*
Omitted. New Clause 13 sets out the provisions for payment which to some extent follow the provisions of Clauses 11(4) and (6) but in this Form apply to all the work since all work is re-measured.

*Clause 13A(2)*
The references are to the Ascertained Final Sum.

*Clauses 15(2) and (3)*
The reference to adjustment of the Contract Sum is omitted and in its place the phrase 'effect shall be given to the Architect's/Supervising Officer's instructions in the calculation of the Ascertained Final Sum' is used.

*Clause 16(e)*
The reference is to 'Tender Price' not 'Contract Sum'.

*Clause 19(2)(c)*
Amounts paid by the Employer are not to be 'included in the calculation of the Ascertained Final Sum'.

*Clause 23(e)*
The reference is to Clause 12(1) not 11(1).

*Clause 23(m)*
A new sub-clause solely applicable to the new Form.

*Clause 24(1)(c)*
The reference is now to the discrepancy or divergence referred to in Clause 1(2) of the new Form. Clause 24(1)(c) does not apply to divergences of quantity.

*Clause 24(1)*
Amounts ascertained are to be 'included in the calculation of the Ascertained Final Sum'.

*Clause 26(2)(b)(ii)*
The reference is to Clauses 13(1)–(4) of the new Form.

*Clause 26(2)(b)(iii)*
The reference is to Clause 13(5) of the New Form.

*Clause 27(g)(i)*
The reference is to Clause 12(3) of the new Form.

*Clause 27(g)(ii)*
The reference is to Clause 12 of the new Form.

*Clause 30(1)*
The words 'whenever the Architect/Supervising Officer considers them necessary' are omitted as valuations are always required for interim payments under the new Form.

*Clause 30(5)*
This sub-clause has been re-drafted and amplified.

*Clause 30(6)(b)*
The reference is to the 'Ascertained Final Sum calculated'.

*Clause 30(7)*
The reference is to the terms of this Contract 'which affect the calculation of the Ascertained Final Sum'.

*Clause 31A*
At beginning of the Clause the references are to 'the prices in the Contract Bills' and to 'an adjustment' which 'shall be made in calculating the Ascertained Final Sum'.

*Clause 31B*
Text omitted. See Practice Note paragraph 17.

*Clause 31C(1) and 31D(1)*
The references to Clause 31B are omitted as Clause 31B is itself omitted.

*Clause 31D(4)*
The reference to Clause 31B is omitted; amounts under Clause 31A and 31C 'shall be taken into account in calculating (a) the Ascertained Final Sum'.

*Clause 31D(4) Proviso(ii)*
Re-drafted.

*Clause 31D(5)*
The reference to Clause 31B is omitted.

*Clause 31D(5)(a)*
The reference is to Clause 13(4) of the new Form.

*Clause 31D(6)*
The reference to Clause 31B is omitted.

*Clause 31E*
The references to Clause 31B are omitted.

*Clause 31F(1)(a)(i)*
The opening words are 'In calculating the Ascertained Final Sum adjustments shall be made'; and the reference to the Formula Rules is subject to the amendments set out in sub-clause (8) (see below).

*Clause 31F(2)(a)*
Paragraph (i) is omitted since the new Form provides for valuations for each interim certificate

*Clause 31F(2)(b), (2)(b)(i), 6(a) and (7)(a)(i)*
The reference to the 'Contract Sum' is omitted.

*Clause 31F(5)(i)*
The references to Part II (i.e. Work Groups) is omitted. See Practice Note paragraph 18.

*Clause 31F(8)*
This sub-clause is new and makes the necessary amendments to the Formula Rules so that they can be used for new Form contracts where Clause 31F of the new Form is required.

*Clause 32(3)*
The reference is to Clause 13(1)–(4) of the new Form.

*Clause 34(3)*
Amounts are to be 'included in the calculation of the Ascertained Final Sum'.

*Clause 35(1)*
The reference is to Clause 30(5)(b) in the new Form.

October 1975


## Practice Note 21

**Sectional Completion Supplement**
Adaptation of the Standard Form of Building Contract WITH Quantities, Private and Local Authorities editions, 1963 (July 1975 Revision) – Additional Clause incorporating modifications for use WHERE THE WORKS ARE TO BE COMPLETED BY PHASED SECTIONS.

(Issued in a Separate Supplement)

**Notes on the use of this supplement**
This Supplement has been drawn up so that it may be used for adapting the Standard Form of Building Contract WITH Quantities as follows:

A. **The Recitals.** In the Contract Form to be adapted —

EITHER (1)

**insert** 'both . . . and the division of the Works into Sections for phased completion (hereinafter referred to as 'Sections')' as shown overleaf.

OR (2)

**strike out** the first page of the Form, **detach** this sheet from the Supplement, **strike out** this page, and **affix** the sheet to the Form so that the adaptation page overleaf may be used as the first page of the Form. If the Form is the **Private edition insert** as appropriate the address or registered office of the Employer and **insert** 'his Architect' at the end of the first recital as shown on the Private edition Form itself; and **delete** the last five lines of the adaptation page (the second recital) which appear at the top of page 2 of the Private edition.

B. **The Articles of Agreement and Annexed Conditions. Detach** the centre page 3–6 of this Supplement, which comprise an additional clause to be inserted in the Articles of the Form, and **affix** those pages between pages 2 and 3 of the Form so as to follow Clause 4 of the Articles and precede the page for signing/sealing.

C. To indicate where the Conditions have been modified by the incorporation of the additional clause and Table of Changes **insert** the symbol (T) (or some other indication) in the margin beside the modified clauses.

D. **Appendix.** Strike out the Appendix in the Contract Form **except the reference to Formula Rules if Clause 31F is to apply** and in substitution detach page 7 of this Supplement, strike out page 8 on the reverse and affix page 7 within the Contract Form.

E. The explanatory notes in Practice note 21 (set out below) are for guidance only and are not intended to form part of the modifications or of the Adapted Contract in which the modifications are incorporated.

**Practice note 21**

1. The Sectional Completion Supplement first issued by the Joint Contracts Tribunal from December 1975 provides for the Standard Form of Building Contract WITH Quantities (Local Authorities and Private Editions 1963, July 1975 Revision) to be adapted so as to be suitable for use where the Works are to be completed by phased sections. The adaptation makes it necessary to substitute, or add a reference to, a 'Section' or 'Sections' in some of the Conditions of the Standard Form where the expression 'the Works' appears. All the adapting modifications are set out seriatim in the Supplement. A Standard Form Contract so adapted is referred to in the following paragraphs as 'the Adapted Contract'.

*Practice*

2. The Adapted Contract is intended for use only where tenderers are notified that the Employer requires the Works to be carried out by phased sections of which the Employer will take possession on Practical Completion of each Section. The Adapted Contract cannot be used for contracts where the Works are not, at the tender stage, divided into Sections in the tender documents. Attention is called to Clause 16 of the Standard Form entitled 'Partial possession by Employer' which is designed to meet those cases where the Adapted Contract has not been used but the Employer nevertheless, by agreement with the Contractor, wishes to take possession of a part of the Works. Where the Adapted Contract is used Clause 16 is suitably modified.

3. It is essential that the tender documents (normally the Contract Drawings and the Bills of Quantities) should identify clearly the Sections which, together, comprise the whole Works. The Sections should then be serially numbered and these Section numbers inserted in the Appendix of the Adapted Contract. In this connection care should be taken, in dealing with any part of the Works which is common to all or several Sections, (such as a boiler-house serving three separate Sections, each comprising a block of flats) to put this part of the Works into a separate Section, and to ascribe to it a Section Value and Date for Possession, Date for Completion, Rate of liquidated Damages for delay and Defects Liability Period.

### The Adaptation

4. The principal modifications to the contract procedures which are connected with the Adapted Contract are the division of the Works into definite Sections in the Contract Documents, coupled with the division of the Contract Sum into corresponding Section Values and the fixing of separate completion periods for each of the Sections. The Adapted Contract remains, however, a single Contract and one final certificate is to be issued at the end; no provision is made for separate final certificates for each Section.

5. The contractual provisions of the Standard Form are, therefore, modified in the Adapted Contract as follows:

### —The Contract Documents

5.1 The recitals to the Articles of Agreement declare that the Contract Drawings and Contract Bills show and describe the division of the Works into Sections. This is followed through into Clause 1(1) of the Conditions which refers to the Appendix in which each Section is identified by reference to the Contract Drawings and Contract Bills.

5.2 The Section Value ascribed to each Section is also entered in the Appendix for the purposes of clauses 16 and 20(A). The term 'Section Value' is defined in Clause 16(e) as 'the value ascribed to the relevant Section in the Appendix', and the relevant Appendix entry indicates that each Section Value is to be the total value of the Section ascertained from the Contract Bills. The Section Values must amount in total to the Contract Sum, and should take into account the apportionment of Preliminaries and other like items priced in the Contract Bills.

5.3 Also to be entered in the Appendix separately for each Section are: Dates for Possession, Dates for Completion, Rates of Liquidated Damages for delay, and Defects Liability Periods.

### —Carrying out the Works

5.4 The Contractor is to be given possession of the site for each of the Sections of the Works. He is then to begin and proceed with each Section concurrently or successively as required by and under the Contract, and to carry out each Section within the contract period stated in the Appendix (Clause 21(1)) or as extended by the Architect* under the Contract (Clause 23). Liquidated damages for delay relate to each Section (Clause 22), and are separately calculated where there is delay in completing any Section.

*—Practical Completion*

5.5 On practical completion of any Section the Architect must issue a Practical Completion certificate for that Section (Clause 15). In consequence the Contractor is relieved of his corresponding duty to insure for that Section under Clause 20(A) (if applicable), and the first moiety of Retention attributable to that Section must be released (Clause 30(4)). A separate Defects Liability Period operates for each Section (Clause 15(2)).

*Final Account*

5.6 When all Sections have been carried out the Architect must issue a certificate to that effect (Clause 15(6)) and the period begins to run within which the final account is to be prepared and the Final Certificate issued for the whole of the Works comprising all the Sections (Clause 30(6)).

*Insurance*

6. The Architect should particularly note that when making insurance arrangements under Clause 19(2)(a) agreement must be reached with the insurers as to whether any Section for which a Practical Completion Certificate has been issued is to be treated as continuing to be included in the Works and so not insured OR is to be treated as 'property other than the Works' and so covered by the insurance.

*APPROXIMATE Quantities Standard Form*

7. The adaptations shown in the Sectional Completion Supplement may also be used in conjunction with the Standard Form of Building Contract for use with Bills of APPROXIMATE Quantities (first issued October 1975), but varied as necessary where there are differences between that Form and the WITH Quantities Form as indicated in the Appendix to Practice note 20.

**\*Footnote:** *In the Local Authorities edition the term 'Supervising Officer' is substituted throughout where the official concerned is not an Architect.*

December 1975

## Practice note 23

### Adjustment of the Contract Sum by means of Formulae: Formula Rules Series 2 dated 4 April 1977

**Note**
This Practice Note includes material published in Practice Note 18 adapted for application to the Series 2 Work Category Indices for the Work Categories 2/1 to 2/48 (see paragraphs 2(*b*) and 3(*c*) of this Practice Note).

**Introduction**

1 Following the Government decision on the use of the Formula Method of calculating fluctuations in public sector work lasting over 12 months (DOE Circular 158/73 of 21.12.73 – 313/73 Welsh Office and SOFD 2/1974 Scottish Office – 'Public Sector Construction Work – Contracting Procedures') the Joint Contracts Tribunal was asked to prepare contractual provisions for the Standard Form of Building Contract where the parties have agreed that fluctuations in costs

during the progress of the contract are not to be dealt with by clauses 31A or 31B (with 31C, D and E) but through the Formulae prepared for NEDO by the EDC for Building for use with indices compiled and maintained by the Property Services Agency (PSA) of the Department of the Environment (DOE) and published as Monthly Bulletins: two sets of Bulletins are issued, one for the original 34 Work Categories and the other (Series 2) for the new 48 Work Categories (see paragraph 2(*b*) below).

A further DOE Circular (19/76 – Welsh Office 24/76) of 10.2.1976 was issued entitled 'Formula Method of Price Variation for Construction Contracts' which formally recommended the use of the NEDO formula in local authority building contracts and set out guidelines in operating this method of price variation.

2 (*a*) The Tribunal therefore issued on 24 March 1975 the following contractual documents:
(1) Clause 31F entitled 'Adjustment of Contract Sum – NEDO Price Adjustment Formula for Building Contracts'.
(2) Standard Form of Building Contract Formula Rules dated 3 March 1975. Notes on clause 31F are set out at appendix A to this Practice Note. (See also Amendment No. 14/1977 in Appendix A referred to in paragraph 2(*b*) of this Note.)

(*b*) The National Consultative Council of the Minister for Housing and Construction set up a Standing Committee on Indices for Building Contracts following publication of the NEDO Formula by the EDC for Building. This Standing Committee is available to deal with problems in the application of the NEDO Formula and has a wide representation for industry, clients and the professions and also two independent academic members. In 1975 the Standing Committee responded to requests from the industry and undertook a review of the Work Categories used in the building formula. This review has now been completed and has resulted in the establishment of new Work Categories totalling 48 for which a new set of Monthly Bulletins (Series 2) is now published. The Standing Committee published in April 1977 its own 'Price adjustment formulae for building contracts (Series 2) – Guide to application and procedure'; and also 'Price adjustment formulae for building contracts (Series 2) – Description of the indices' which replace the two similar guides published by NEDO in 1974. The Tribunal has, therefore, had to review Clause 31F and the Formula Rules referred to above in order to ensure that they are suitable for contracts for which the Work Categories (Series 2) are to be used. The Tribunal, therefore, published on 6 May 1977, the following contractual documents:
1. Amendment No. 14/1977 – Clause 31F (reproduced at the end of Appendix A).
2. Formula Rules – Work Category Indices Series 2 dated 4 April 1977.
Both documents are *only* suitable for contracts where formula adjustment is by reference to the 48 Work Categories for which Series 2 Indices are being published.

3 (*a*) The Tribunal decided that the detailed application of the Formula Method required a set of rules which could more appropriately be published as a

separate document rather than as a part of the Contract clause. Clause 31F, therefore, refers in sub-clause (1)(*a*)(i) to the Formula Rules as an integral part of the clause. **The Rules issued by the Tribunal thus become contractually binding upon the parties where clause 31F has been included as part of a building contract using the Standard Form.**

(*b*) The Rules dated 3 March 1975 were derived trom the Building EDC's 'Price Adjustment Formulae for building contracts. A guide to the practical application of the formula' and an acknowledgement to the EDC's work is made in the Rules. The EDC guide is not a legal document however and is not tied to any particular application of the formula method; in particular the guide sets out various alternatives with which contract documents have to deal specifically. Clause 31F and the Formula Rules therefore provide a definite code; and where alternatives are available it is provided that the Contract Bills must state which alternative is to apply.

(*c*) The Rules (Series 2) are derived from the NCC Standing Committee on Indices for Building Contracts booklet 'Price adjustment formulae for building contracts (Series 2) – Guide to application and procedure' and an acknowledgment to the Standing Committee's works is made in these Rules. The Standing Committee's Guide is not a legal document, however, and is not tied to any particular application of the Formula Method; in particular the Guide sets out various alternatives with which contract documents have to deal specifically. Clause 31F, as amended, and the Formula Rules (Series 2) therefore provide a definite code; and where alternatives are available it is provided that the Contract Bills must state which alternative is to apply.

**Formula Rules – Work Category Indices Series 2**

4 The Formula Rules set out the method of adjusting the Contract Sum at each interim valuation by adjusting the Value of Work included in that valuation in accordance with the movement of the Index Numbers in the Monthly Bulletins (Series 2) referred to above. The Rules also cover adjustment of any value of work included in Certificates after Practical Completion and in the Final Certificate. The prices of some work and items in the Contract Bills are not subject to formula adjustment and this work and items are identified in rules 4, 14 and 17. The Rules are divided into two sections, and the second section consists of three parts.

*Section 1* sets out those Rules which are applicable to adjustment whether under Part I, Part II or Part III of Section 2. Attention is called to the Definitions in rule 3, which apply to both the Rules and clause 31F, and these should be carefully studied. In *Section 2*, Part I and Part II are mutually exclusive and the Bills of Quantities must state which Part will apply. Adjustment under either Part is by reference to the Index Numbers for the 48 Work Categories set out at appendix A to the Rules. Part III applies to work to be executed by the Contractor or a non-nominated sub-contractor (defined in the Rules as 'Contractor's Specialist Work') for which specialist indices are compiled and maintained by the PSA of the DOE and published in the Monthly Bulletins referred to above. Where a nominated sub-contract so provides these specialist indices are also applicable to that specialist engineering work which the Contract Bills state is to be executed by a nominated sub-contractor (see also paragraphs 11 and 12).

5 The operation of the Formulae depends on the work and other items set out in the Bills of Quantities having been annotated or scheduled by the Quantity Surveyor before tenders are invited so that the following four divisions are easily identified by the tenderers:

   (i)   that work which is to be allocated to the Work Categories set out in appendix A to the Rules;

   (ii)  that work to be carried out by the Contractor (or by a non-nominated sub-contractor) which is not covered by the Work Categories but to which one of the specialist formulae referred to in Part III of the Rules applies. This is defined in rule 3 as 'Contractor's Specialist Work';

   (iii) that work which is to be subject to adjustment but which is neither allocated to a Work Category nor designated as Contractor's Specialist Work; this becomes the 'Balance of Adjustable Work';

   (iv)  that work etc. which is specifically designated in rules 4, 14 and 17 as not being subject to formula adjustment.

For the treatment of Provisional Sums see rules 16 and 17.

In addition it is necessary that the Bills shall have been drawn up so that when they are priced and have thus become the Contract Bills, those Bills and also the other contract documents comply with:

   Rule 3: the Base Month to be recorded in the Appendix to the Conditions;
   Rule 3 (Local Authority edition): the amount of the Non-adjustable Element;
   Rule 7: which method of adjustment to the price of structural steel work is to apply;
   Rule 8: the method of adjusting for 'fix-only' work;
   Rule 10: whether part I applies;
   Rules 11 and 19: completion of the Schedule identifying the Work Category for each relevant Bill item, the Contractor's Specialist Work etc.;
   Rule 27*b*: materials or goods for which the Employer requires special treatment;
   Rule 30: whether Part II applies;
   Rule 43: a statement of the weighting of labour and materials for certain Contractor's Specialist Work (electrical and heating ventilating and air conditioning);
   Rule 58 (Lift installations): the element of the Contract Sum which is subject to formula adjustment;
   Rule 64 (Structural steelwork installations): a statement of the average price per tonne included in the Contract Sum for steel delivered to fabricator's works and the average price per tonne included in the Contract Sum for erection of steelwork.
   Rule 70*a* (Catering Equipment Installations): the apportionment of the value of each item for catering equipment installations contained in the Contract Bills between (i) materials and shop fabrication (ii) supply of factor items and (iii) site installation.

6 Parts I and II prescribe from the tender stage to the final account the procedural and other steps which have to be taken by the parties in order to calculate the adjustment of the Contract Sum by reference to the Formula set out in rule 9 where Part I applies or that in rule 29 where Part II applies. Special provisions

apply for any valuations after the month in which the Certificate of Practical Completion is issued (see rules 28 and 49): see paragraph 18.

7 The *Part 1 Formula* applies where tenders have been obtained on the basis that the Value of Work (as defined in rule 3) within any one of the Work Categories is to be adjusted by reference to the monthly movement of the Index Number relating to that Work Category.

8 The *Part II Formula* applies where tenders have been obtained on the basis that the Work Categories are to be combined into various Work Groups and that adjustment of the Value of Work for each Work Group will then be by reference to a special Work Group Weighted Index derived from the Work Category Index Numbers in accordance with the provisions of rule 34. The weightings are fixed at the commencement of the contract by reference to the total value of the work in the Contract Bills allocated to each Work Category in a Work Group. In this connection such factors as the phasing of the works and the extent of different constructional types within the contract may affect a decision to have a single set of weightings for the whole project or separate sets for different parts of the project. The weightings are not to be altered even if, as a result for instance of variation, the relative values change during the contract. Where such changes occur as a result of variation instructions the provision of clause 11(6) may be relevant.

9 The *Formulae in Part III* apply for adjusting the value of any Contractor's Specialist Work. These five Formulae cover electrical installations; heating ventilation and air conditioning installations; lift installations; structural steelwork installations and catering equipment installations. In regard to *structural steelwork* it is also possible for the value of such installations carried out by the Contractor (or a non-nominated sub-contractor) to be adjusted by reference to the movement of the index for Work Category 23; and by rule 7 of Section 1 of the Rules the Contract Bills must state whether formula adjustment of the value of structural steelwork installations to be carried out by the Contractor (or by a non-nominated sub-contractor) is to be made by using the specialist Formula in rule 63 or by reference to the index for Work Category 23.

10 Contractor's Specialist Work is always adjusted by reference to the relevant Formula in Part III whether Part I or Part II is applicable to adjustment of the Value of Work in the Work Categories and in the Balance of Adjustable Work. (For structural steel installations however Work Category 23 can be used if this is made clear at the tender stage: see rule 7.)

**Nominated sub-contractors**
11 Where work is to be executed by a nominated sub-contractor the sub-contract to which clause 27(a) refers will have to reflect any prior agreement reached between the nominated sub-contractor and the Architect/Supervising Officer on behalf of the Employer on how the price for such work is to be adjusted in respect of fluctuations. Where Formula adjustment has been agreed then the adjustment will be *either* by reference to one of the five specialist Formulae which are set out in rules 50, 54, 58, 63 and 69 where the work is within the operation of those specialist engineering formulae; *or* by reference to the relevant Work Category Index Number(s) which will have had to be agreed between the sub-contractor and

the Architect/Supervising Officer on behalf of the Employer and then included in the relevant nominated sub-contract.

12 The Tribunal has been informed that, pending publication by the Tribunal of a form for sub-contractors nominated under the provisions of Standard Form, the NFBTE, FASS and CASEC have prepared appropriate formula adjustment provisions for the 'Standard Form of Sub-Contract; for use where the sub-contractor is nominated under the 1963 Edition of the Standard Form of Building Contract' (the 'Green Form') both for the original system and for the Series 2 Work Categories.

### Private and Local Authorities WITH Quantities editions

13 Clause 31F and the Formula Rules apply to both the Local Authorities and the Private WITH quantities editions of the Standard Form but the 'non-adjustable element', defined in rule 3, applies only to the Local Authorities edition (DOE Circular 158/73 (313/73 Welsh Office) as amended by DOE Circular 19/76 (24/76 Welsh Office) makes this abatement of the amount of the formula adjustment mandatory for the public sector work to which that circular refers). The Private edition still follows the recommendation in paragraph 1.19 of the EDC for Building 'Guide to the practical application of the formulae' (referred to in para. 3(*b*) above) that formula adjustment should be reimbursed in full. (Note: For the application of the Formula in contracts let under the JCT Standard Form for use with Bills of Approximate Quantities see Practice Note 20, paragraph 18.)

### Tender price level

14 As stated in rule 18 the price level of a tender or contract let on the Standard Form to which formula adjustment is to apply is deemed to be represented by the firm Work Category Index Numbers published in the Monthly Bulletins for the Base Month. This Base Month has to be stated in the tender documents and subsequently recorded in the appendix to the Contract Conditions. The Index Numbers are first published in the Monthly Bulletins as provisional; and then, usually some three months later, a firm Index Number is substituted (which may merely confirm that the provisional Index Number should now be regarded as firm).

15 Under rules 23, 36, 53, 57, 61, 66 (but see Notes to rules 61*c* and 66*b*) and 75 it is provided that adjustment for each Valuation Period will throughout the contract be initially by reference to the provisional Index Numbers including, until the firm Base Month Index Numbers are available, the provisional Index Numbers for the Base Month; and that any correction necessary after publication of the firm Index Numbers will be made in a subsequent certificate.

### Productivity deduction

16 Not now applicable: abolished with effect from 1 August 1976.

### Interim valuations

17 Attention is called to the Definitions in rule 3 of the Formula Rules of 'Valuation Period' and 'Value of Work', The Valuation Period is the interval between the valuations on which two consecutive interim certificates are based and Value of Work is the difference between the total valuation at the end of a Valuation Period

and that ascertained at the end of the previous Valuation Period. Clause 31F and the Formula Rules do not require the parties to identify when work covered by an interim valuation was carried out as the relevant factor for formula adjustment under these provisions is when that work is first included in a valuation; formula adjustment is then applied by using the provisional (and later the firm) Index Numbers applicable at the Midpoint of the Valuation Period. Apart from the change of firm for provisional, Index Numbers are not to be changed unless it is discovered that incorrect Index Numbers have been used and/or a correction is subsequently made in accordance with rule 5. If therefore there is an under or over valuation or an error in the computation of the total value, which is compensated in a subsequent valuation, the Index Numbers relevant to the latter valuation would be applied; there is no question of applying the Index Numbers for the Valuation Period in which the work was done.

18 Attention is called to rules 28 and 49 on the treatment of any value not previously subject to formula adjustment and which is certified in those interim certificates which, under clause 30(1) as amended by clause 31F(2)(a)(ii), are issued after the month in which the Certificate of Practical Completion is issued and included in the measurement and valuation for preparing the final account for the issue of the final certificate. This value is adjusted on the 'average' basis set out in these rules. **The system of formula adjustment should be so operated that the amount of value which has to be adjusted under these rules is kept to the minimum.** Amounts included in Interim and Final Certificates in respect of the release of retentions are not subject to formula adjustment since adjustment has already been calculated on the full amount.

**Examples**
19 To assist users of the Standard Form examples of how clause 31F and the Formula Rules are intended to work in practice are given in a separate Tribunal publication 'Fluctuations Formulae Example'.

**Part III Specialist Formulae**
20 In explanation of certain rules in Part III the following information (taken from the NCC Standing Committee Guide referred to in paragraph 3(*c*), is included in appendices:

Appendix B, rule 45*b*:
A note on the index for average earnings for the Formulae for lift installations and structural steelwork installations.

Appendix C, rule 51:
List of items and the proportions used in the index for labour and of the weightings in the index for materials for the Formula for electrical installations.

Appendix D, rule 55:
List of items and the proportions used in the index for labour for the Formula for heating and ventilating and air conditioning installations.

Appendix E, rule 65*b*:
Statement of the items included in the index for materials for use with the Formula for structural steelwork installations and their weighting.

**Appendices to Practice note 23**

**Appendix A**

**Notes on Clause 31F**
(See also Amendment 14/1977 dated April 1977 reproduced on page 9. These Notes are to be read subject to this Amendment.)

*Clause 31F*
The clause is drafted as a further part of clause 31. Formula adjustment, being an adjustment of value and not referable in any way to actual costs incurred or saved, requires the total deletion of Parts A to E which are related to fluctuations in various actual costs. With the deletion of clause 31D containing the definition of 'Date of Tender' it was necessary to provide an identical definition in rule 3 of the Formula Rules; see sub-clause (1)(*b*) which makes the Definitions in the Rules applicable to clause 31F and several of the expressions so defined occur in the clause (e.g. Monthly Bulletins, Valuation Period).

*Sub-clause (1)(a)(i)*
This paragraph makes the Formula Rules part of the Contract Conditions. The 'date of tender' is defined in rule 3 of the Formula Rules (see sub-clause (1)(b)). The Rules are dated by reference to a day and month and any subsequent editions will be similarly so dated.

*Sub-clause (1)(a)(ii)*
This paragraph is for the avoidance of doubt and confirms that adjustment is to sums exclusive of VAT.

*Sub-clause (1)(c)*
The text within the first parenthesis is only applicable to the Local Authorities edition and empowers the reduction of the amount of adjustment by the Non-Adjustable Element. The second parenthesis makes clear that no adjustment is to be made to sums of retention released under clauses 16(*f*) or 30(4).

*Sub-clause (1)(d)*
This paragraph must be read in conjunction with rule 5; see paragraph 17 of the Practice Note.

*Sub-clause (2)(a) and (b)*
This sub-clause amends clauses 30(1), (2) and (3) by reference. No actual amendments are therefore needed. The reasons for the deemed additions and deletion are set out in this subclause. The amendment in sub-clause (2)(*a*)(ii) is to ensure that the last Interim Certificate issued at the Period of Interim Certificates will include normal formula adjustment under Part I rule 9 or Part II rule 29 even if it is issued after the Certificate of Practical Completion. Certificates issued thereafter will contain adjustments under the 'average' basis referred to in paragraph 18 of the Practice Note.

*Sub-Clause (2)(c)*
This paragraph which amends clause 35(2) by reference would enable any dispute as

to whether the Contractor was in default over completion for the purposes of operating sub-clause (7), to be opened earlier than Practical Completion of the Works.

*Sub-clause (2)(d)*
This paragraph is needed since clause 13A(3) only refers to the definition of 'date of tender' in clause 31D(6)(*a*) and 31D will have been deleted where clause 31F is used.

*Sub-clause (3)*
This sub-clause provides that when the Contract Bills require the Contractor to use manufactured articles specially purchased outside the U.K. (whose price is unlikely to be reflected in the Work Category Index Numbers) fluctuations for these articles shall be adjusted by reference to market price changes and not by formula.

*Sub-clause (4)(a)*
This paragraph makes clear that clause 31F and the Formula Rules do not apply to work carried out by nominated sub-contractors whose recovery of fluctuations is to be dealt with by whatever provision has been agreed between the Architect/Supervising Officer on behalf of the Employer and the sub-contractor and included in the relevant sub-contract. Adjustments to the nominated sub-contract sum under such provision will be reflected in the main contract sum by virtue of clause 30(5)(*c*). See paragraphs 11 and 12 of this Practice Note.

*Sub-clause (4)(b)*
This provision is intended to make clear that if formula adjustment is agreed between the contractor and a non-nominated sub-contractor then the only formula adjustment appropriate for such sub-contracts is by reference to the relevant Work Category/Work Categories or to one of the specialist formulae (which are the same as those set out in Part III of the Rules).

*Sub-clause (5)*
Attention is called to the two provisos to which any agreements between the Contractor and the Quantity Surveyor on varying the mechanics of operating formula adjustment are subject.

*Sub-clause (6)*
As the Contractor will have tendered on the basis that the Value of Work for each Valuation Period will be adjusted under clause 31F and the Rules, provision was needed for the situation where the Index Numbers cease temporarily or for a longer period to be available. In these circumstances a fair and reasonable adjustment is made.

*Sub-clause (7)*
The Standard Form does not provide for cessation of payment of fluctuations under clauses 31A or 31B (with 31C, D and E) during the period when the Contractor is, or is alleged to be, in default over completion. Where clause 31F is used *paragraph* (a) provides that adjustment during a period of default over completion is by reference to the firm Index Numbers applicable to the Valuation Period during which the

Contractor became in default. *Paragraph (b)* makes the operation of paragraph *(a)* conditional on the use of clause 23 (extension of time) unamended and with the specific inclusion of clause 23(j)(i) and (ii) (shortages of labour and materials). The reason for this condition is that with the new provisions of paragraph *(a)* it is necessary for full provisions in regard to extension of time to be included in the contract. *Paragraph (c)* deals with any similar limitation in formula adjustment of the sub-contract sum for nominated sub-contractors and provides that the application of any such limitation to the nominated sub-contract formula adjustment is quite independent of the operation of paragraph *(a)* on adjustments made in respect of work carried out by the main contractor; and will require appropriate provisions also in the nominated sub-contract.

*Appendix: Rule 3*
The Base Month will normally be the month preceding that during which tenders have to be returned. It is, however, open to the parties to specify a different Base Month and the actual month chosen must be set out in this appendix.

*Amendments to the Standard Form of Building Contract 1963 edition (July 1976 Revision) Private and Local Authorities editions With Quantities and With Approximate Quantities (1975 edition as revised)*
The amendments relating to the Standard Form of Building Contract 'With Quantities' and 'With Approximate Quantities', Local Authorities and Private Editions, set out below are hereby incorporated in this Contract and the provisions of the Articles of Agreement and the annexed Conditions shall have effect as so amended.
**Explanatory Note:** *These amendments are made in conjunction with the publication of the JCT Formula Rules Series 2 April 1977 and in consequence of the amendments to the Formula contained in 'Price adjustment formulae for building contracts (series 2) – Guide to application and procedure', prepared by the National Consultative Council Standing Committee on Indices for Building Contracts and published by HMSO.*

*Clause 31F – Adjustment of Contract Sum – NEDO Price Adjustment Formulae for Building Contracts*

1. First side heading and footnote:
   **Delete** 'NEDO'

2. Sub-paragraph (4)(a)(i):
   **Delete** the whole sub-paragraph and **substitute:**
   '(i) in the case of electrical installations, heating and ventilating and air conditioning installations, lift installations, structural steelwork installations and in the case of catering equipment installations, the relevant specialist formula (see the Formula Rules, rule 50, rule 54, rule 58, rule 63 and rule 69);'

3. Sub-paragraph (4)(b)(i):
   **Delete** the whole sub-paragraph and **substitute:**
   '(i) in the case of electrical installations, heating and ventilating and air conditioning installations, lift installations, structural steelwork installations and in the case of catering equipment installations, the relevant specialist formula;'

4. Paragraph (7)(c):
   In line 1 **delete** '(b)(ii)' and **insert** '(b)(i)'.


## Appendix B

### A note on the index for average earnings (rule 45b) for the Formulae for lift installations and structural steelwork installations

(*Source: Paragraphs 5.06 and 5.07 of NCC Standing Committee on Indices for Building Contracts 'Price adjustment formulae for building contracts (Series 2) – Guide to application and procedure' 1977.*)

Two indices measuring changes in the cost of labour in (*a*) the mechanical engineering industries and (*b*) the electrical engineering industries, have been constructed. These are based on the index of average earnings and the index of average weekly hours worked which are published in tables 127 and 121 respectively of the Department of Employment Gazette. Both the cost indices can be used in the formula for lift installations but only that based on mechanical engineering is to be used in the structural steel formula.

The data used relate to the earnings of all employees in mechanical engineering and electrical engineering and are linked with the index of weekly hours worked by operatives in the engineering, shipbuilding, electrical goods and other metal goods industries to smooth the effects of short-time, overtime, etc on earnings. In addition, because the indices in table 127 are subject to a degree of seasonal fluctuation, a four month moving average is applied to the resulting data. Both these adjustments are shown in the table below.

Example of adjustment of *index numbers* in table 127/121 by four month moving average (mechanical engineering)

| 1975 | table $\frac{127†}{121‡} \times 100$ | Adjustment by four month moving average |
|---|---|---|
| April | 225.5 | |
| May | 225.7 | |
| June | 231.9 | 230.9* |
| July | 240.4 | 233.9* |
| August | 237.6 | |

Lastly the indices for mechanical engineering and electrical engineering are adjusted to take account of the contractor's statutory obligations in his capacity as an employer i.e. employer's liability insurance, annual and public holidays, national insurance contribution and CITB levy.

†Index of average earnings mechanical engineering
‡Index of average hours worked by operatives in engineering, shipbuilding, electrical goods and other metal goods industries
*The calculated average of any four months is allotted to the third month of the four

**Appendix C**

**List of items and proportions used in the index for labour and of the weightings in the index for materials for the Formula for electrical installations (rule 51)**
*(Source: Paragraphs 5.18 and 5.19 of the NCC Standing Committee 'Price adjustment formulae for building contracts (Series 2) – Guide to application and procedure' 1977.)*

(i)  The index for labour is related to the National Working Rules and Industrial Determinations of the Joint Industry Board for the Electrical Contracting Industry (England and Wales) for Labour in Zone B.

Contractors engaged in electrical installation work in Scotland are reminded that while they are obliged to comply with the National Working Rules and Industrial Determinations of the SJIB for the Electrical Contracting Industry, the Rules or the Industrial Determinations of the two Boards, although normally similar, are unlikely to be identical at any given point in time. Accordingly, they should carefully note that changes in the labour index will be related to decisions of the JIB (England and Wales) and that promulgations of the SJIB will not be separately reflected in the index.

The Index for labour includes the following in the proportions given below:
1  Hours worked: 50 hours at standard basic wage rate
2  Non-productive overtime: 4 hours at the standard basic wage rate
3  Guaranteed time: 2% addition to items 1, 2 and 6
4  Employers' Liability: ¾% addition to items 1, 2 and 6
5  National Insurance: statutory contribution on items 1, 2, 6 and 11
6  Weekly Supplement
7  Redundancy Fund: statutory payment (included in the National Insurance contribution) only
8  Lodging, subsistence and travelling: assuming that:
    (*a*)  1/3 operatives are in receipt of Lodging Allowance, including entitlement to periodic fares, but excluding any entitlement to daily local fares
    (*b*)  1/3 operatives are in receipt of Country Allowance
    (*c*)  1/3 operatives travel daily (10–15 miles single journey)
9  Holidays with pay⎫ Annual cost of the weekly stamp apportioned over 49
10  Sick pay　　　⎭ productive weeks
11  Public holidays: 8 days of basic working week at standard basic wage rate apportioned over 49 productive weeks
12  Training levy: the annual levy apportioned over 49 productive weeks.

*Notes:*
1.  The monthly labour *index numbers* reflect changes in the above constituents as and when they have occurred, and will reflect any further changes which may occur in the future, together with any additional factors affecting the cost of labour as they are introduced. The details of the constituents given are those current at the time of preparation of this booklet.

2.  There is no provision in the formula for special reimbursement of Determination No. 2 payments. These should therefore be included in the tender price. They will then be subject to formula adjustment in the normal way.

The proportions of each grade of operative used in the index:

|  | Weighting % |
|---|---|
| Approved electricians (with responsibility money) | 10 |
| Approved electricians | 50 |
| Electricians | 35 |
| Apprentice electricians (50% of electrician's rate) | 5 |
|  | 100% |

(ii) Items and weightings used in electrical installations

| Resource index | | Weighting % |
|---|---|---|
| 3122.000 | Electrical conduit tubes | 2.8 |
| 3695.900 | Electrical cable trunking fittings and conduit fittings | 6.4 |
| 3112.100 | Steel sheets* | 10.8 |
| 3612.500 | Switchfuses and distribution equipment for commercial and industrial installations | 10.0 |
| 3612.200 | Starting and control gear | 2.0 |
| 3695.210 | Wiring accessories | 3.0 |
| 3623.000 | Mains cable | 14.0 |
| 3625.000 | General wiring cables | 14.0 |
| 3623.500 | Cable jointing accessories | 3.5 |
| 3221.500 | Copper sheet and strip† | 3.5 |
| 3695.260 | Commercial and industrial light fittings | 30.0 |
|  | | Total 100.0 |

* Representing light steel constructions and cable trays
† Representing copper tape


**Appendix D**

**List of items and the proportions used in the index for labour for the Formula for heating ventilating and air conditioning installations (rule 55)**
(*Source: Paragraphs 5.29 and 5.30 of NCC Standing Committee on Indices for Building Contracts 'Price adjustment formulae for building contracts (Series 2) – Guide to application and procedure' 1977.*)

(i) The index for labour is related to the National Agreement in the Heating, Ventilating, Air-Conditioning, Piping and Domestic Engineering Industry for Labour in Grade B Regions and includes the following in the proportions given below:
    1 Hours worked: 50 hours at standard basic wage rate
    2 Non-productive overtime: 2½ hours at the standard basic wage rate
    3 Guaranteed Time: 2% addition to items 1, 2 and 6
    4 Employers' Liability: ¾% addition to items 1, 2 and 6

5 National Insurance: statutory contribution on items 1, 2, 6 and 11
6 Weekly Supplement
7 Redundancy Fund: statutory payment (included in the National Insurance contribution) only
8 Lodging, subsistence and travelling: assuming that:
   (a) 1/3 operatives are in receipt of Lodging Allowance, including entitlement to periodic fares, but excluding any entitlement to daily local fares
   (b) 1/3 operatives are in receipt of Radius Allowance (i.e. exceeding 30 miles)
   (c) 1/3 operatives travel daily (10–15 miles single journey)
9 Holidays with pay ⎱ Annual holiday stamp apportioned over 49 productive
10 Sick pay ⎰ weeks
11 Public holidays: 8 days of basic working week at standard basic wage rate apportioned over 49 productive weeks
12 Training levy: the annual levy apportioned over 49 productive weeks.

*Note*

The monthly labour indices since base date (1970 = 100.0) reflect changes in the above constituents as and when they have occurred, and will reflect any further changes which may occur in the future, together with any additional factors affecting the cost of labour as they are introduced. The details of the constituents given above are those current at the time of preparation of this booklet.

The proportions of each grade of operative used in the index:

|  | Weighting % |
|---|---|
| Foreman | 6.1 |
| Chargehand | 11.1 |
| Advanced fitter/welder (gas and arc) | 5.3 |
| Advanced fitter/welder (gas or arc) | 7.7 |
| Advanced fitter | 9.8 |
| Fitter/welder (gas and arc) | 5.9 |
| Fitter/welder (gas or arc) | 7.1 |
| Fitter | 15.2 |
| Improver | 5.0 |
| Assistant | 12.2 |
| Mate | 14.6 |
|  | 100.0% |

(ii) The index for materials used in the heating, ventilating and air-conditioning formula is as follows. This index contains a small weighting in respect of labour employed (in the factory) in the manufacture of ductwork.

| nent | Resource index | | Weighting % |
|------|----------------|---|-------------|
| er Plant | 3411.100 | Shell Boilers | 1 |
| | 3394.250 | Heating Boilers—Industrial | 8 |
| | 3394.210 | Heating Boilers—Domestic | 2 |
| rifiers | 3415.300 | Heat exchangers | 2 |
| trol Systems | 3542.130 | Thermostats, Temperature Indicators | 1 |
| | 3542.190 | Flow, Level and other Measuring and Indicating Instruments | 2 |
| | 3613.100 | A C Electric Motors 1–10 HP | 2 |
| | 3612.500 | Switchfuses and Distribution Equipment for Commercial and Industrial Installations | 5 |
| twork | 3112.170 | Galvanised Steel Sheet | 6 |
| | (PSA(DOE) Labour Index No. 3) | Labour in Fabrication | 6 |
| s etc. | 3394.110 | Industrial fans and Ventilating Units | 15 |
| work | 3221.400 | Copper Tubes | 7 |
| | 3121.000 | Steel Tubes (other than Electric Conduit Tubes) | 6 |
| | 3123.000 | Pipe Fittings | 4 |
| ps | 3331.200 | Centrifugal, Turbine and Axial Flow Pumps | 3 |
| iators | 3394.400 | Heating Radiators | 4 |
| rigeration Plant | 3393.000 | Commercial and Industrial Refrigeration Machinery | 7 |
| ks etc. | 3997.200 | Galvanised Tanks, Cisterns and Cylinders | 1 |
| rmal Insulation erials | 4631.100 | Glass Fibre and Glass Fibre Products | 6 |
| ves | 3332.000 | Industrial Valves | 4 |
| er | 3394.500 | Miscellaneous Space Heating, Ventilating and Air-Conditioning Equipment | 8 |
| | | | 100% |

**Appendix E**

**Statement of the items included in the index for materials for use with the Formula for structural steelwork installations and their weighting (rule 65b)**

(*Source: Paragraph 5.47 of NCC Standing Committee on Indices for Building Contracts 'Price adjustment formulae for building contracts (Series 2) – Guide to application and procedure' 1977.*)

The items included in the index and their weightings are as follows:

*Items and weighting used in steelwork installations*

| Type | Size (mm) | Weighting % |
|------|-----------|-------------|
| Plate | 10 × 2500 × 6000 | 12.0 |
| | 12.5 × 2500 × 12000 | 11.0 |
| | 15 × 2500 × 10000 | 5.0 |
| | 25 × 2500 × 16000 | 11.0 |
| | 50 × 2500 × 16000 | 8.5 |
| Beams | 914 × 419 × 18288 | 19.0 |
| | 610 × 229 × 13716 | 8.0 |
| Columns | 203 × 203 × 12188 | 6.0 |
| Flats | 75 × 12 × 6100 | 6.5 |
| Channels | 203 × 89 × 9141 × 8 | 4.5 |
| Angles | 60 × 60 × 9141 × 8 | 8.5 |
| | Total | 100.0% |

# Appendix C: General Conditions of Government Contracts for Building and Civil Engineering Works

Form GC/Works/1
Edition 2, September 1977

*This publication is Crown Copyright and has been reproduced by kind permission of the Controller of Her Majesty's Stationary Office.*

**Definitions, etc.**

1 (1) 'the Contract' means the documents forming the tender and acceptance thereof, together with the documents referred to therein including these Conditions (except as set out in the Abstract of Particulars), the Specification, the Bills of Quantities and the Drawings, and all these documents taken together shall be deemed to form one contract. When there are no Bills of Quantities all reference to Bills of Quantities in the Contract shall be treated as cancelled, except that where the context so admits the Schedule of Rates shall be substituted therefor.

(2) In the Contract the following expressions shall, unless the context otherwise requires, have the meanings hereby respectively assigned to them:–

'the accepted risks' means the risks of–

(a) fire or explosion,

(b) storm, lightning, tempest, flood or earthquake,

(c) aircraft or other aerial devices or objects dropped therefrom, including pressure waves caused by aircraft or such devices whether travelling at sonic or supersonic speeds,

(d) ionising radiations or contamination by radioactivity from any nuclear fuel or from any nuclear waste from the combustion of nuclear fuel,

(e) the radioactive, toxic, explosive or other hazardous properties of any explosive nuclear assembly or nuclear component thereof.

(f) riot, civil commotion, civil war, rebellion, revolution, insurrection, military or usurped power or King's enemy risks (within the definition of that expression contained in section 15(1)(a) of the War Risks Insurance Act 1939 as for the time being in force);

'the Authority' means the person so designated in the Abstract of Particulars;

'Bills of Quantities' includes Provisional Bills of Quantities and Bills of Approximate Quantities;

'the Contract Sum' means the sum accepted, or the sum calculated in accordance with the prices accepted, by the Authority as payable to the Contractor for the full and entire execution and completion of the Works before taking into account the effect of Conditions 9, 11G, 38, 39, 50 and 53;

'the Contractor' means the person or persons whose tender is accepted by the Authority and his or their legal personal representatives or permitted assigns;

'the date for completion' shall be the date set out in or ascertained in accordance with the Abstract of Particulars or the date on which such extension or extensions of time (if any) as the Contractor may be allowed under the provisions of these Conditions shall expire;

'the Final Account' means the document prepared by the Quantity Surveyor showing the calculation of the Final Sum;

'the Final Sum' means the amount payable under the Contract by the Authority to the Contractor for the full and entire execution and completion of the Works;

'the Quantity Surveyor' means the person so designated in the Abstract of Particulars;

'the Schedule of Rates' means the Authority's Schedule of Rates in the form stated in the tender or the Contractor's Schedule of Rates provided in accordance with Condition 5B;

'the Site' means the land or place where work is to be executed under the Contract and any adjacent land or place which may be allotted or used for the purpose of carrying out the Contract;

'the SO' means the person designated as the Superintending Officer in the Abstract of Particulars;

'the Works' means the works described in the Specification and/or Bills of Quantities and/or shown on the Drawings, including all modified extra or additional works to be executed under the Contract.

(3) In these Conditions, references to things for incorporation are references to things for incorporation in the Works and references to things not for incorporation are references to things provided for the execution of the Works but not for incorporation therein.

(4) Any decision to be made by the Authority under the Contract may be made by any person or persons authorised to act for him for that purpose and may be made in such manner and on such evidence or information as he or such person or persons shall think fit.

(5) The headings to these Conditions shall not affect the interpretation thereof.

(6) Any notice to be given under the Contract shall be in writing, typescript or printed and if sent by registered post or recorded delivery to the last known place of abode or business of the Contractor shall be deemed to have been served on the date when in the ordinary course of post it would have been delivered to him.

### Contractor deemed to have satisfied himself as to conditions affecting execution of the Works

2 (1) The Contractor shall be deemed to have satisfied himself as regards existing roads, railways, or other means of communication with and access to the Site, the contours thereof, the risk of injury or damage to property adjacent to the Site or to the occupiers of such property, the nature of the materials (whether natural or otherwise) to be excavated, the conditions under which the Works will have to be carried out, the supply of and conditions affecting labour, the facilities for obtaining any things whether or not for incorporation and generally to have obtained his own information on all matters affecting the execution of the Works

and the prices tendered therefore except information given or referred to in the Bills of Quantities which is required to be given in accordance with the method of measurement expressed in the Bills of Quantities.

(2) No claim by the Contractor for additional payment will be allowed on the ground of any misunderstanding or misinterpretation in respect of any such matter nor shall the Contractor be released from any risks or obligations imposed on or undertaken by him under the Contract on any such grounds or on the ground that he did not or could not forsee any matter which might affect or have affected the execution of the Works.

**Vesting of Works etc in the Authority. Things not to be removed**
**3** From the commencement to the completion of the Works, the Works and any things (whether or not for incorporation) brought on the Site in connection with the Contract and which are owned by the Contractor or vest in him under any contract shall become the property of and vest in the Authority subject to his right of rejection of any things for incorporation which are not approved, but the Authority shall not, subject to the provisions of Conditions 26 and 50, be responsible or chargeable for any thing lost, stolen, damaged, destroyed or removed from the Site or that shall fail in any way and the Contractor shall be responsible for the protection and preservation of the Works and any things (whether or not for incorporation) brought on the Site until the termination of the Contract.

(2) None of the things referred to in paragraph (1) above which are brought on the Site shall be removed therefrom without the consent in writing of the SO, but the SO may order or permit the Contractor in writing at any time during the progress of the Works to remove from the Site any such things which are unused and thereupon the Contractor shall forthwith remove the same and upon removal the property shall revest in the Contractor. The decision of the SO upon any matter arising under this paragraph shall be final and conclusive.

**Specifications, Bills of Quantities and Drawings**
**4** (1) In case of discrepancy between these Conditions and the Specification and/or the Bills of Quantities and/or the Drawings, the provisions of these Conditions shall prevail.

(2) Figured dimensions on the Drawings shall be followed in preference to the scale.

(3) The SO shall provide free to the Contractor three copies of the Contract Drawings and of the Specification and of the blank Bills of Quantities, and two copies of all further drawings issued during the progress of the Works. The Contractor shall keep one copy of all Drawings and of the Specification on the Site and the SO or his representative shall at all reasonable times have access to them.

(4) The Specification, the Bills of Quantities, the Drawings and all copies thereof and extracts therefrom shall if required be returned to the SO on the completion of the Works or the earlier determination of the Contract.

**Bills of Quantities (applicable if so stated in the tender)**

**5** (1) The Bills of Quantities shall be deemed to have been prepared in accordance with the principles of the method of measurement expressed therein, except where otherwise stated.

(2) Any error in description or in quantity in the Bills of Quantities or any omission therefrom shall not vitiate the Contract nor release the Contractor from his obligation to execute the whole or any part of the Works according to the Drawings and Specification or from any of his obligations or liabilities under the Contract, but where the Contract Sum is based upon the quantities in the Bills of Quantities the error shall be rectified and the rectification dealt with under Condition 9(1) and the value thereof shall be added to or deducted from the Contract Sum as the case may be:
Provided that there shall be no rectification of any errors, omissions or wrong estimates in the prices inserted by the Contractor in the Bills of Quantities or in his computations therein or calculations thereon.

(3) The quantities given in Provisional Bills of Quantities or Bills of Approximate Quantities shall not be held to gauge or limit the amount and description of the work to be executed by the Contractor.

**The Authority's Schedule of Rates (applicable if so stated in the tender)**

**5A** The descriptions of work given in the Authority's Schedule of Rates shall not define or limit the work to be executed under the Contract.

**The Contractor's Schedule of Rates**

**5B** If neither Bills of Quantities nor the Authority's Schedule of Rates are provided in respect of the Works or in respect of any work or things to which Condition 38 applies the Contractor shall, if required by the Authority, supply forthwith to the Authority a full and detailed Schedule of Rates which was properly and reasonably used for calculating the Contract Sum or sub-contract sum.

**Progress of the Works**

**6** Possession of the Site or the order to commence shall be given to the Contractor by notice and the Contractor shall thereupon commence the execution of the Works and shall proceed with diligence and expedition in regular progression or as may be directed by the SO under Condition 7 so that the whole of the Works shall be completed by the date for completion.

**SO's instructions**

**7** (1) The Contractor shall carry out and complete the execution of the Works to the satisfaction of the SO who may from time to time issue further drawings, details and/or instructions, directions and explanations (all of which are hereafter referred to as 'the SO's instructions') in regard to:

    (a)  the variation or modification of the design, quality or quantity of the Works or the addition or omission or substitution of any work;

    (b)  any discrepancy in or between the Specification and/or Bills of Quantities and/or Drawings;

    (c)  the removal from the Site of any things for incorporation which are brought thereon by the Contractor and the substitution therefor of any other such things;

(d)  the removal and/or re-execution of any work executed by the Contractor;

(e)  the order of execution of the Works or any part thereof;

(f)  the hours of working and the extent of overtime or nightwork to be adopted;

(g)  the suspension of the execution of the Works or any part thereof;

(h)  the replacement of any foreman or person below that grade employed in connection with the Contract;

(i)  the opening up for inspection of any work covered up;

(j)  the amending and making good of any defects under Condition 32;

(k)  the execution in an emergency of work necessary for security;

(l)  the use of materials obtained from excavations on the Site;

(m)  any other matter as to which it is necessary or expedient for the SO to issue instructions, directions or explanations.

(2)  If any of the SO's instructions issued orally have not been confirmed in writing by him such confirmation shall be given upon a reasonable request by the Contractor made within fourteen days of the issue of such instructions.

(3)  The decision of the SO that any such instructions are necessary or expedient shall be final and conclusive and the Contractor shall forthwith comply therewith.

(4)  The Contractor shall not make any alteration in, addition to or omission from the Works described in the Specification and/or Bills of Quantities and/or shown on the Drawings except in pursuance of the SO's instructions issued in accordance with this Condition and such alterations, additions or omissions shall not invalidate the Contract.

### Failure of Contractor to comply with SO's instructions

8  If the Contractor, after receipt of a notice from the SO requiring compliance with any of the SO's instructions within a period to be specified in the notice by the SO, fails to comply with such instruction, the Authority may, without prejudice to the exercise of his powers under Condition 45, provide labour and/or any things (whether or not for incorporation), or enter into a contract for the execution of any work which may be necessary to give effect thereto and any additional costs and expenses incurred by the Authority in connection therewith over and above those which would have been incurred had the Contractor complied with such instruction shall be recoverable from the Contractor.

### Valuation of the SO's instructions

9  (1)  The value of alterations in, additions to and omissions from the Works made in compliance with the SO's instructions shall be added to or deducted from the Contract Sum, as the case may be, and shall be ascertained by the Quantity Surveyor as follows:–

(a)  by measurement and valuation at the rates and prices for similar work in the Bills of Quantities or Schedules of Rates in so far as such rates and prices apply;

(b)  if such rates and prices do not apply, by measurement and valuation at rates and prices deduced therefrom in so far as it is practicable to do so;

(c)  if such rates and prices do not apply and it is not practicable to deduce rates and prices therefrom, by measurement and valuation at fair rates and prices; or

    (d)  if the value of alterations or additions cannot properly be ascertained by measurement and valuation, by the value of the materials used and plant and labour employed thereon in accordance with the basis of charge for daywork described in the Contract:

Provided that where an alteration in or addition to the Works would otherwise fall to be valued under sub-paragraph (a) or (b) above but the Quantity Surveyor is of the opinion that the instruction therefor was issued at such a time or was of such content as to make it unreasonable for the alteration or addition to be so valued, he shall ascertain the value by measurement and valuation at fair rates and prices.

(2)  (a)  If the Contractor–
      (i)  properly and directly incurs any expense beyond that otherwise provided for in or reasonably contemplated by the Contract in complying with any of the SO's instructions (other than instructions for alterations in, additions to or omissions from the Works), or
      (ii)  can reasonably effect any saving in the cost of the execution of the Works in or as a result of complying with any of the SO's instructions,
    the Contract Sum shall, subject to sub-paragraph (b) of this paragraph and to Condition 23, be increased by the amount of that expense, or shall be decreased by the amount of that saving, as ascertained by the Quantity Surveyor.
  (b)  It shall be a condition precedent to the Contract Sum being increased under sub-paragraph (a) of this paragraph that–
      (i)  the SO's instruction shall have been given or confirmed in writing;
      (ii)  as soon as reasonably practicable after incurring the expense the Contractor shall have provided such documents and information in respect of the expense as he is required to provide under Condition 37(2); and
      (iii)  the instruction shall not have been rendered necessary as a result of any default on the part of the Contractor.

(3) If any alterations or additions (other than those authorised to be executed by daywork) have been covered up by the Contractor without his having given notice in pursuance of the provisions of Condition 22 of his intention to do so, the Quantity Surveyor shall be entitled to appraise the value thereof and his decision thereon shall be final and conclusive.

**Valuation by measurement**

**10** When the Contract is based upon Provisional Bills of Quantities, Bills of Approximate Quantities or the Schedule of Rates the value of the whole of the work executed to the satisfaction of the SO shall be ascertained by measurement and valuation in accordance with Condition 9(1) (except as may otherwise be provided in respect of any item to which Condition 38 applies).

**11A to F (Separate Condition, applicable if so stated in the Abstract of Particulars)**

**Variation of price (Labour-tax matters)**

**11G(1)** In this Condition:
    (a)  'workpeople' means persons employed directly by the Contractor on the

Site on manual labour, whether skilled or unskilled, and includes such persons chargeable to overheads, and 'workperson' means one of such persons.

(b) 'labour-tax matter' means any tax levy or contribution (including National Insurance contributions but excluding Value Added Tax, Income Tax and any levy payable under the Industrial Training Act 1964) which is by law payable by the Contractor in respect of his work-people and any premiums and refunds which are by law payable to the Contractor in respect of his workpeople.

(2) (a) If, as a result of the coming into effect after the date for return of tenders of any change in the level of any labour-tax matter or any change in the incidence of any labour-tax including the imposition of any new such matter or the abolition of any such matter previously existing, the cost to the Contractor of performing his obligations under the Contract is increased or decreased the Contract Sum shall, subject to the provisions of these Conditions, be increased or decreased, as the case may be, by the net additional cost or the net saving which the Contractor thereby incurs or makes.

(b) Where any workperson is employed by the Contractor in any week partly on the Site and partly off the Site, there shall only be taken into account for the purpose of calculating in respect of that workperson any increases or decreases in the Contract Sum under paragraph (2)(a) of this Condition one fifth of any additional costs or savings incurred or made by the Contractor in respect of a change in a labour-tax matter for each day in that week on which that workperson is employed by the Contractor on the Site provided that if such workperson is so employed for more than five days in that week any such additional days shall be disregarded for this purpose.

(3) Subject to the provisions of this Condition, the Contract Sum shall be reduced by the maximum amount which the Contractor could save by securing all the reductions obtainable in the prices payable under the provisions of any sub-contracts (being sub-contracts which involve the carrying out of work by a sub-contractor on the Site) by reason of such provisions being included therein in pursuance of Condition 30(3) and shall be increased by the amount which the Contractor necessarily spends in meeting the increases payable under such provisions by reason of their being so included.

(4) (a) The Contractor shall, within a reasonable time, give notice to the SO of any changes mentioned in paragraph (2) of this Condition giving rise to additional costs or savings in respect of any workpeople and of any such reductions obtainable or increases payable in sub-contract prices as are mentioned in paragraph (3) of this Condition and shall thereafter furnish such further information on these matters as the Authority may require.

(b) The Contractor shall keep such books, accounts, and other documents and records as are necessary to show the additional costs or savings relevant for the purposes of paragraph (2) of this Condition and shall at the request of the Authority furnish, verified in such manner as the Authority may require, any accounts, documents or records so kept and such other information as the Authority may reasonably require.

    (c) The decision of the Authority as to the amount of any variation in the Contract Sum to be made under this Condition shall be final and conclusive. Unless the parties otherwise agree, any increase or decrease in the Contract Sum shall be adjusted on the completion of the Contract.

**Setting out Works**

**12** The S O shall supply dimensioned drawings, levels and other information necessary to enable the Contractor to set out the Works. The Contractor shall set out the Works in accordance therewith and shall provide all necessary instruments, profiles, templates and rods and be solely responsible for the correctness of such setting out. The Contractor shall provide, fix and be responsible for the maintenance of all stakes, templates, profiles, levelmarks, points and such other setting out apparatus as may be required, and shall take all necessary precautions to prevent their removal, alteration or disturbance and shall be responsible for the consequences of such removal, alteration or disturbance and for their efficient reinstatement.

**Things for incorporation and workmanship to conform to description**

**13** (1) All things for incorporation shall be of the respective kinds described in the Specification and/or Bills of Quantities and/or Drawings and the Contractor shall upon the request of the S O prove to the S O's satisfaction that such things do so conform.

(2) The S O and his representative shall have power at any time to inspect and examine any part of the Works or any thing for incorporation either on the Site or at any factory or workshop or other place where any such part or thing is being constructed or manufactured or at any place where it is lying or from which it is being obtained, and the Contractor shall give all such facilities as the S O or his representative may require to be given for such inspection and examination.

(3) The S O shall be entitled to have tests made of any things for incorporation supplied. For this purpose the Contractor shall, subject to any provision to the contrary, provide all facilities that the S O may require. Where procedures are provided for or referred to in the Specification regarding specific tests the same shall be complied with. If at the discretion of the S O an independent expert is employed to make any such tests as are referred to in this paragraph, his charges shall be borne by the Contractor only if the tests disclose that such things are not in accordance with the provisions of the Contract. The report of the independent experts shall be final and conclusive.

(4) The Works shall be executed in a workmanlike manner and to the satisfaction in all respects of the S O. If any things for incorporation do not accord with the provisions of the Contract or if any workmanship does not so accord the same shall at the cost of the Contractor be replaced, rectified or reconstructed as the case may be, and all such things which are rejected shall be removed from the Site.

**Local and other authorities' notices and fees**

**14** The Contractor shall (so far as may be applicable to the Works) give all notices required by any Act of Parliament (whether general, local or personal) or by the regulations and/or bye-laws of any local authority and/or of any public service, company or authority affected by the Works or with whose systems the same are or will be connected, and he shall pay and indemnify the Authority against any fees or changes demandable by law under such Acts, regulations and/or bye-laws in respect of the Works and shall make and supply all drawings and plans required in connection with any such notices.

### Patent rights

**15** All royalties, licence fees or similar expenses in respect of the supply or use for or in connection with the Works of any invention, process, drawing, model, plan or information shall be deemed to have been included in the Contract Sum and the Contractor shall indemnify the Authority from and against all claims and proceedings, which may be made or brought against the Authority and any damages, costs and expenses incurred by the Authority by reason of such supply or use:

Provided that where such supply or use has been necessary in order to comply with any instructions given by the S O under the Contract, any royalty, licence fee or similar expense payable by the Contractor in respect of such supply or use and not provided for or reasonably contemplated by the Contract, shall be deemed for the purpose of Condition 9(2) to be an expense properly and directly incurred in complying with an S O's instruction other than one for an alteration in, addition to, or omission from the Works.

### Appointment of Resident Engineer or Clerk of Works

**16** The Authority may appoint a Resident Engineer or a Clerk of Works and the Contractor shall admit him and his assistants to the Site. The Resident Engineer or Clerk of Works may exercise all the powers of the S O under Condition 13(1) and (2) and such other powers of the S O under the Contract as the S O may give notice of to the Contractor. The exercise of or failure to exercise such powers by the Resident Engineer or the Clerk of Works shall in no way limit or vary the ability of the S O to exercise such powers subsequently.

### Watching, lighting and protection of Works

**17** The Contractor shall provide all watchmen necessary for the protection of the Site, the Works, and of all things (whether or not for incorporation) on the Site, during the progress of the execution of the Works, and shall be solely responsible for and shall take all reasonable and proper steps for protecting, securing, lighting and watching all places on or about the Works and the Site which may be dangerous to his workpeople or to any other person.

### Precautions to prevent nuisance

**18** The Contractor shall take all reasonable precautions to prevent a nuisance or inconvenience to the owners, tenants or occupiers of other properties and to the public generally and to secure the efficient protection of all streams and waterways against pollution.

### Removal of rubbish

**19** The Contractor shall at all times keep the Site free from all rubbish and debris arising from the execution of the Works.

**Excavations and material arising therefrom**

**20** (1) Subject to the provisions of paragraph (2) of this Condition, material of any kind obtained from the excavations shall remain the property of the Authority. Such material shall be dealt with as provided in the Contract, but the SO shall have power to direct its use in the Works or disposal by other means. When the Authority's property is permitted to be used in substitution for any things (whether or not for incorporation) which the Contractor would otherwise have provided the Quantity Surveyor shall ascertain the amount of any saving in the cost of the execution of the Works and the Contract Sum shall be reduced by the amount of any such saving.

(2) All fossils, antiquities and other objects of interest or value which may be found on the Site or in carrying out excavations in the execution of the Works shall (so far as may be) remain or become the property of the Authority, and upon discovery of such an object the Contractor shall forthwith–

(a) use his best endeavours not to disturb the object;
(b) cease work if and in so far as the continuance of work would endanger the object or prevent or impede its excavation or its removal;
(c) take all steps which may be necessary to preserve the object in the exact position and condition in which it was found; and
(d) inform the SO of the discovery and precise location of the object.

(3) The SO shall issue instructions in regard to what is to be done concerning an object the finding of which is reported to him by the Contractor under paragraph (2) of this Condition, which may include instructions requiring the Contractor to permit the examination, excavation or removal of the object by a third party.

**Foundations**

**21** The Contractor shall not lay any foundations until the excavations for the same have been examined and approved by the SO.

**Contractor to give due notice prior to covering work**

**22** The Contractor shall give reasonable notice to the SO whenever any work or thing for incorporation is intended to be covered in with earth or otherwise, and in default of so doing shall, if required by the SO, uncover such work and thing at his own expense.

**Suspension for frost, etc**

**23** If the SO shall be of the opinion that the execution of the Works or any part thereof should be suspended to avoid risk of damage from frost, inclement weather or other like causes, then, without prejudice to the responsibility of the Contractor to make good defective and/or damaged work, the SO shall have power to instruct the Contractor to suspend the execution of the Works or any part thereof and the Contractor shall not resume work so suspended until permitted to do so by the SO. The Contractor shall not be entitled to any increase in the Contract Sum under Conditions 9(2) or 53(1) in respect of any expense incurred in consequence of any such instruction unless he can show that he has complied with all the requirements of the Specification relating to the avoidance of damage due to frost, inclement weather or other like causes.

**Daywork**

**24** The Contractor shall give to the SO reasonable notice of the commencement of any work ordered to be executed by daywork and shall deliver to the SO within one week of the end of each pay week vouchers in the form required by the SO giving full detailed accounts of labour, materials and plant for that pay week. A copy of each voucher, if found correct, will be certified by the SO and returned to the Contractor.

**Precautions against fire and other risks**

**25** (1) The Contractor shall take all reasonable precautions to prevent loss or damage from any of the accepted risks, and to minimise the amount of any such loss or damage or any loss or damage caused by a servant of the Crown. The Contractor shall comply with such instructions to this end as may be given to him from time to time in writing by the SO.

(2) The Contractor shall comply with any statutory regulations (whether or not binding on the Crown) which govern the storage·of explosives, petrol, or other things (whether or not for incorporation) which are brought on the Site.

**Damage to Works or other things**

**26** (1) All things not for incorporation which are on the Site and are provided by or on behalf of the Contractor for the construction of the Works shall stand at the risk and be in the sole charge of the Contractor, and the Contractor shall be responsible for, and with all possible speed make good, any loss or damage thereto arising from any cause whatsoever, including the accepted risks.

(2) (a) The Contractor shall (unless the Authority exercises his powers to determine the Contract) with all possible speed make good any loss or damage arising from any cause whatsoever occasioned to the Works or to any things for incorporation on the Site (including any things provided by the Authority) and shall notwithstanding such loss or damage proceed with the execution and completion of the Works in accordance with the Contract.

   (b) The cost of making good such loss or damage shall be wholly borne by the Contractor, save that–

   (i) where the loss or damage is wholly caused by the neglect or default of a servant of the Crown acting in the course of his employment as such, the Authority shall pay the Contractor for making good the loss or damage, and where it is partly caused by such neglect or default, the Authority shall pay the Contractor such sum as is proportionate to that servant's share in the responsibility for the loss or damage, and

   (ii) where the loss or damage is wholly caused by any of the accepted risks the Authority shall pay the Contractor for making good the loss or damage and where it is partly so caused the Authority shall pay the Contractor such sum as is proportionate to the share of any of the accepted risks in causing the loss or damage.

   (c) Any sum payable by the Authority under sub-paragraph (2)(b) of this Condition shall be ascertained in the same manner as a sum payable in respect of an alteration or addition under the Contract and shall be added to the Contract Sum.

### Assignment or transfer of Contract

**27** The Contractor shall not, without the consent in writing of the Authority, assign or transfer the Contract, or any part, share or interest therein. No instalment or other sum of money to become payable under the Contract shall be payable to any other person than the Contractor unless the consent of the Authority in writing to the assignment or transfer of such money to such person be produced when such payment is claimed as due.

### Date for completion: Extensions of time

**28** (1) The Works shall be carried on and completed to the satisfaction of the SO and all unused things for incorporation and all things not for incorporation, the removal of which is ordered by the SO, shall be removed and the Site and the Works cleared of rubbish and delivered up to his satisfaction on or before the date for completion.

(2) The Contractor shall be allowed by the Authority a reasonable extension of time for the completion of the Works in respect of any delay in such completion which has been caused or which the Authority is satisfied will be caused by any of the following circumstances–

(a) the execution of any modified or additional work;

(b) weather conditions which make continuance of work impracticable;

(c) any act or default of the Authority;

(d) strikes or lock-outs of workpeople employed in any of the building, civil engineering or analogous trades in the district in which the Works are being executed or employed elsewhere in the preparation or manufacture of things for incorporation;

(e) any of the accepted risks; or

(f) any other circumstance which is wholly beyond the control of the Contractor:

Provided that–

(i) except in so far as the Authority shall otherwise decide, it shall be a condition upon the observance of which the Contractor's right to any such extension of time shall depend that the Contractor shall, immediately upon becoming aware that any such delay has been or will be caused, give notice to the SO specifying therein the circumstances causing or likely to cause the delay and the actual or estimated extent of the delay caused or likely to be caused thereby;

(ii) the Contractor shall not be entitled to any extension of time in respect of a delay caused by any circumstance mentioned in sub-paragraph (2)(f) of this Condition if he could reasonably be expected to have foreseen at the date of the Contract that a delay caused by that circumstance would, or was likely to, occur;

(iii) in determining what extension of time the Contractor is entitled to the Authority shall be entitled to take into account the effect of any authorised omission from the Works;

(iv) it shall be the duty of the Contractor at all times to use his best endeavours to prevent any delay being caused by any of the above-mentioned circumstances and to minimise any such delay as may be caused thereby and to do all that may reasonably be required, to the satisfaction of the SO, to proceed with the Works; and

(v) the Contractor shall not be entitled to an extension of time if any such delay is attributable to any negligence, default or improper conduct on his part.

## Partial possession before completion

**28A** (1) The Authority may, before the completion of the Works, take possession of any part of the Works (in this Condition referred to as a 'completed part') which is certified by the S O as having been completed to his satisfaction and is either–
(a) a section specified in the Abstract of Particulars; or
(b) a part of the Works (including a part of a section) in respect of which the parties agree, or the S O has given an instruction, that possession shall be given before the completion of the Works;
and such completed part, on and after the date on which the certificate is given, shall no longer be deemed to form part of the Works for the purposes of Conditions 3 and 26.

(2) The provisions of Condition 32 shall have effect in relation to a completed part as if the maintenance period or periods in respect of the completed part or any subcontract works comprised therein, commenced on the date of certification under paragraph (1) of this Condition.

(3) As soon as possible after certification under paragraph (1) of this Condition the S O shall certify the value of the completed part for the purposes of paragraphs (4) and (5) of this Condition.

(4) The provisions of Condition 29 shall have effect notwithstanding that the Authority has taken possession of a completed part, but–
(a) where the completed part comprises part of the Works but not a section or part of a section, the rate of liquidated damages specified in the Abstract of Particulars in respect of the Works shall be reduced by an amount bearing the same ratio to the specified rate as the value of the completed part bears to the Contract Sum; and
(b) where the completed part comprises part of a section, the rate of liquidated damages specified in the Abstract of Particulars in respect of that section shall be reduced by an amount bearing the same ratio to the specified rate as the value of the completed part bears to such sum representing the value of the relevant section as shall be determined by the S O.

(5) The reserve accumulated in accordance with Condition 40(1) shall be apportioned by the Authority as at the date of certification under paragraph (1) of this Condition in such manner that the share of the reserve apportioned in respect of a completed part shall bear the same ratio to the whole of the reserve as the value of the completed part bears to such sum representing the value of the Works as shall be estimated by the S O at that date, and the Authority shall pay to the Contractor–
(a) one half of the share so apportioned in respect of the completed part on certification; and
(b) the remaining one half of that share, when the S O has certified, after the end of the maintenance period in respect of the completed part, that the Works comprising the completed part are in a satisfactory state.

(6) Any decision of the S O under this Condition shall be final and conclusive.

**Liquidated damages**

**29** (1) If the Works shall not be completed and the Site cleared on or before the date for completion, the Contractor shall pay to the Authority liquidated damages in respect of the delay in completion calculated in accordance with the details set out in the Abstract of Particulars for the period during which the Works shall remain uncompleted and the Site not cleared after the date for completion.

(2) No payment or concession to the Contractor or order for modified or additional work at any time given to the Contractor or other act or omission of the Authority or his servants shall in any way affect the right of the Authority to recover the said liquidated damages or shall be deemed to be a waiver of the right of the Authority to recover such damages unless such waiver has been expressly stated in writing signed by or on behalf of the Authority.

(3) If at any time the Authority (whether or not he has previously allowed the Contractor any extension of time under Condition 28) gives notice to the Contractor that, in the opinion of the Authority, the Contractor is not entitled to any or (as the case may be) any further extension, then any sum which at that time would represent the amount of liquidated damages payable by the Contractor under this Condition or this Condition as modified by Condition 28A(4) (as the case may be) shall be treated for the purposes of Condition 43 as a sum recoverable from or payable by the Contractor.

**Sub-letting**

**30** (1) The Contractor shall not sub-let any part of the Contract without the previous consent in writing of the SO.

(2) In every case of sub-letting in connection with the Contract the Contractor shall enter into a sub-contract which, in addition to the power to determine referred to in Condition 44(6) shall include–

    (a) a provision to the effect that from the commencement to the completion of the sub-contract all things for incorporation belonging to the person who enters into the sub-contract which are brought on the Site in connection with the sub-contract shall vest in the Contractor subject to any right of the Contractor to reject the same;

    (b) such provisions as may be necessary to enable the Contractor to fulfil his obligations to the Authority under the Contract, including the obligations of the Contractor under Conditions 3(2), 4(4), 13(2) and (3), 35, 51, 56, 57 and 58;

    (c) such provisions as will impose on the person who enters into the sub-contract liabilities similar to those imposed on the Contractor by Conditions 27, 36, 55 and 59; and

    (d) a provision to the effect that no part of the sub-contract work shall be further sub-let without the consent of the Contractor.

(3) In the case of a sub-contract which involves the execution of work on the Site, the Contractor shall also include provisions similar to those in Condition 11G(1) and (2).

(4) Without prejudice to the obligations of the Contractor under any of the provisions of the Contract, the Contractor shall, whenever so requested by the Authority, take such action as shall be necessary to secure that a person who has entered into a sub-contract complies with and performs all obligations imposed upon him pursuant to paragraph (2) of this Condition.

**Sub-contractors and suppliers**

**31** (1) No person against whom the Contractor shall make reasonable objection shall be employed as a nominated sub-contractor or nominated supplier upon or in connection with the Works.

(2) The Contractor shall be responsible for any sub-contractor or supplier employed by him in connection with the Works whether he shall be nominated or approved by the Authority or the SO, or shall be appointed by the Contractor in accordance with the directions of the Authority or the SO or otherwise.

(3) The Contractor shall make good any loss suffered or expense incurred by the Authority by reason of any default or failure, whether total or partial, on the part of any sub-contractor or supplier.

**Defects liability**

**32** (1) This Condition applies–
    (a) to any defects (excluding any defects specified in sub-paragraph (b) below) which may appear within the maintenance period specified in the Abstract of Particulars in respect of the Works; and
    (b) to any defects in any sub-contract works in respect of which a separate sub-contract maintenance period is specified in the Abstract of Particulars, which may appear within the appropriate sub-contract maintenance period,

being (in either case) defects which arise from any failure or neglect on the part of the Contractor or any sub-contractor or supplier in the proper performance of the Contract or from frost occurring before completion of the Works.

(2) The Contractor shall make good at his own cost to the satisfaction of the SO any defects to which this Condition applies:

Provided that he shall not be required to make good at his own cost any damage by frost which may appear after completion unless the cause of such damage arose at a time before completion.

(3) In case of default the Authority may provide labour and/or any things necessary, or may enter into a contract or contracts, in order to repair and make good any defects to which this Condition applies, and all costs and expenses consequent thereon shall be borne by the Contractor and shall be recoverable from the Contractor by the Authority.

(4) In the case of any defects specified in paragraph (1)(b) of this Condition which have been made good, the provisions of paragraphs (2) and (3) of this Condition shall apply to the sub-contract works which have been made good until the expiration of either the appropriate sub-contract maintenance period or a period of six months from the date of making good (whichever is the later).

**Contractor's agent**

**33** The Contractor shall employ a competent agent to whom directions may be given by the SO. The agent shall superintend the execution of the Works generally with such assistance in each trade as the SO may consider necessary. Such agent shall be in attendance at the Site during all working hours except that when required to do so he shall attend at the office of the SO.

### Daily returns

**34** The Contractor's agent shall provide the S O each day with a distribution return of the number and description of workpeople employed on the Works.

### Contractor to conform to regulations

**35** Where the Works are to be executed within the boundaries of a Government Establishment, the Contractor shall comply with those Rules and Regulations of the Establishment which are described in the Contract.

### Replacement of Contractor's employees

**36** (1) The S O shall have power to require the Contractor, subject to compliance with any statutory requirements, immediately to cease to employ in connection with the Contract and to replace any foreman or person below that grade whose continued employment thereon is in the opinion of the S O undesirable.

(2) The Authority shall have power to require the Contractor immediately to cease to employ in connection with the Contract and to replace any person above the grade of foreman, including the Contractor's agent, whose continued employment in connection therewith is in the opinion of the Authority undesirable.

(3) Any decision of the Authority or the S O under this Condition shall be final and conclusive.

### Attending for measurement and provision of information

**37** (1) The Contractor's representative shall from time to time, when required on reasonable notice by the Quantity Surveyor, attend at the Works to take jointly with the Quantity Surveyor any measurements of the work executed that may be necessary for the preparation of the Final Account. Any such measurements when ascertained and any differences arising thereon shall be recorded in the manner required by the Quantity Surveyor. The Contractor shall without extra charge provide assistance with every appliance and other thing necessary for measuring the work. If the Contractor's representative fails to attend when so required, the Quantity Surveyor shall have power to proceed by himself to take such measurements.

(2) The Contractor shall provide to the Quantity Surveyor all documents and information necessary for the calculation of the Final Sum (including for Conditions 9, 20 and 53) certified in such manner as the Quantity Surveyor may require.

### Prime Cost items

**38** (1) The words 'Prime Cost' or the initials 'PC' applied in the Contract to any work to be executed or any things to be supplied by a sub-contractor or supplier shall mean that in respect of such an item the sum to be paid by the Authority shall be the sum (inclusive of proper charges for packing, carriage and delivery to the Site) due to the sub-contractor or supplier, after adjustment in respect of over-payment or over-measurement or otherwise and after deduction of all discounts obtainable for cash in so far as such discounts exceed $2\frac{1}{2}$ per cent and of all trade discounts, rebates and allowances.

(2) The Contractor shall also be entitled to payment for fixing in accordance with the rates included in the Bills of Quantities or the Schedule of Rates and to Contractor's profit where applicable. The payment for fixing shall cover unloading, getting in, unpacking, return of empties and other incidental expense. The Contractor's profit at the rate included in the Bills of Quantities or the Schedule of Rates shall be adjusted pro rata on the prime cost excluding any alterations in that prime cost due to the operation of any conditions incorporated in the sub-contract pursuant to Condition 30(3).

(3) Any increases or decreases in the prime cost sums included in the Contract resulting from these adjustments shall be added to or deducted from the Contract Sum. The Contractor shall produce to the Quantity Surveyor such quotations, invoices and bills (properly receipted) as may be necessary to show the actual details of the sums paid by the Contractor.

(4) All prime cost items shall be reserved for the execution of work or the supply of things by persons to be nominated or appointed in such ways as may be directed by the Authority or the SO and the Contractor shall not order work or things under such items without the written instruction of the SO or consent of the Authority. The Authority reserves the right to order and pay for all or any part of such items direct and to deduct the sums included therefor from the Contract Sum less an amount in respect of Contractor's profit at the rate included in the Bills of Quantities or Schedule of Rates adjusted pro rata on the amount paid direct by the Authority.

(5) In the event of the termination of a sub-contract to which this Condition applies, the Contractor shall, subject to the consent in writing of the Authority, either select another sub-contractor or supplier to undertake or complete the execution of work or the supply of things in question, or himself undertake or complete the execution of the work or the supply of those things and the Authority shall pay the Contractor the sum which would have been payable to him under paragraph (1) of this Condition if termination of the said sub-contract had not occurred, together with any allowances for profit and attendance which are contained in the Bills of Quantities.

**Provisional sums and provisional quantities**
**39** The full amount of the provisional lump sums included in the Contract and the net value annexed to each of the provisional items inserted in the Bills of Quantities shall be deducted from the Contract Sum and the value of work ordered and executed thereunder shall be ascertained as provided by Conditions 9(1) or 10 as the case may be. No work under these items is to be commenced without instructions in writing from the SO.

**Advances on account**
**40** (1) The Contractor shall be entitled to be paid during the progress of the execution of the Works 97 per cent of the value of the work executed on the Site to the satisfaction of the SO and the Authority shall accumulate the balance as a reserve.

(2) The Contractor shall also be entitled to be paid during the progress of the execution of the Works 97 per cent of the value of any things for incorporation

which are in the opinion of the SO in accordance with the Contract and which have been reasonably brought on the Site and are adequately stored and protected against damage by weather or other causes, but which have not at the time of the advance been incorporated in the Works. When any things on account of which an advance has been made under this paragraph are incorporated in the Works the amount of such advance shall be deducted from the next payment made under paragraph (1) of the Condition.

(3) The Contractor may at intervals of not less than one month submit claims for payment of advances on account of work done and of things for incorporation which have been delivered. Such claims shall be supported by a valuation of the work done and of things so delivered, which valuation shall be made on the basis of the rates in the Bills of Quantities or in the Schedule of Rates or, where such rates are not applicable, on the appropriate alternative basis of valuation set forth in Conditions 9(1) or 10. When the valuation has been agreed by the SO, the SO shall certify the sum to be paid by way of advance:
Provided that if the Contract Sum exceeds £100,000 there shall be paid to the Contractor on his application at the end of the second week in each monthly period an interim advance on account of the further work done or things for incorporation supplied since the date of the last valuation. The amount of any such interim advance shall be an approximate estimate only and the decision of the SO in regard thereto shall be final and conclusive.

(4) Any sum agreed to be credited by the Contractor for old materials may be deducted from the first or any subsequent advance.

(5) Without prejudice to the Contractor's entitlement to an increase in the Contract Sum under Conditions 9(2) or 53(1), to the Authority's entitlement to a decrease in that sum under Condition 9(2), or to the amount of any such increase or decrease, where the SO is of the opinion that there is to be any such increase or decrease he shall decide an amount to be added on account of that increase, or to be deducted on account of that decrease, to or from any sum falling to be paid to the Contractor under paragraph (3) of this Condition and a sum equal to the amount so decided shall be added or deducted, as the case may be, to or from a sum falling to be so paid.

(6) Before the payment of any advance or the issue of the final certificate for payment the Contractor shall, if requested by the SO, satisfy him that any amount due to a sub-contractor or supplier of things for incorporation which is covered by any previous advance has been paid. In any case where the SO is not satisfied as aforesaid–
   (a)   the Authority may withhold payment to the Contractor of the Amount in question until the SO is so satisfied; and
   (b)   in the case of a nominated sub-contractor or supplier, if the SO certifies that the amount in question has not been paid, the Authority may pay to the sub-contractor or supplier the whole or part of any such amount, which shall thereupon be immediately recoverable by the Authority from the Contractor.
The decision of the SO as to whether any such amount has not been paid and of the Authority as to the sum (if any) to be paid to the nominated sub-contractor or nominated supplier shall be final and conclusive.

(7) In paragraph (6) of this Condition, the expression 'nominated sub-contractor or nominated supplier' means a person with whom the Contractor, in compliance with a nomination by the SO or the Authority, has entered into a contract for the execution of work or the supply of things designated as a 'Prime Cost' or 'PC' item in accordance with Condition 38.

## Payment on and after completion

**41** (1) Upon the completion of the Works to the satisfaction of the SO the Contractor shall be entitled to be paid the amount which the Authority estimates will represent the Final Sum less one half the amount of the reserve, and thereafter the Authority may, if he thinks fit, pay further sums in reduction of the reserve.

(2) As soon as possible after the completion of the Works to the satisfaction of the SO the Quantity Surveyor shall forward one copy of the Final Account to the Contractor.

(3) If after the end of the maintenance period specified in the Abstract of Particulars the SO has certified that the Works are in a satisfactory state, and the Final Sum has been calculated and agreed (or in default of agreement has been determined by an arbitrator appointed under Condition 61) then–
  (i) if the Final Sum exceeds the total amount paid to the Contractor, the excess shall be paid to the Contractor by the Authority; or
  (ii) if the total amount paid to the Contractor exceeds the Final Sum, the excess shall be paid to the Authority by the Contractor.

(4) If the Final Sum has been calculated and agreed before the end of the said maintenance period, then–
  (i) if the balance of that sum due to the Contractor exceeds any reserve which the Authority is for the time being entitled to retain, that excess shall be paid to the Contractor by the Authority; or
  (ii) if the total amount paid to the Contractor exceeds the Final Sum, the excess shall be paid by the Contractor to the Authority.

## Certificates

**42** (1) The SO shall from time to time certify the sums to which the Contractor is entitled under Conditions 40 and 41. The SO shall also certify the date on which the Works are completed to his satisfaction and after the end of the said maintenance period he shall issue a certificate when the Works are in a satisfactory state.

(2) Any interim certificate relating to payment for work done or things for incorporation delivered may be modified or corrected by any subsequent interim certificate or by the final certificate for payment, and no interim certificate of the SO shall of itself be conclusive evidence that any work or things to which it relates are in accordance with the Contract.

(3) Any dispute as to the Contractor's right to a certificate or as to the sums to be certified from time to time, shall be referred to the Authority whose decision shall be final and conclusive:

Provided that this paragraph shall not apply to a dispute–

(i) as to a matter in respect of which Condition 40 provides for the decision of the SO to be final and conclusive;

(ii) as to the Contractor's right to a certificate regarding the satisfactory state of the Works after the end of the maintenance period; or

(iii) as to the amount of the balance of the Final Sum due to the Contractor.

### Recovery of sums due from the Contractor

**43** Whenever under the Contract any sum of money shall be recoverable from or payable by the Contractor such sum may be deducted from or reduced by the amount of any sum or sums then due or which at any time thereafter may become due to the Contractor under or in respect of the Contract or any other contract with the Authority or with any Department or Office of Her Majesty's Government.

### Special powers of determination

**44** (1) The Authority shall, in addition to any other power enabling him to determine the Contract, have power to determine the Contract at any time by notice to the Contractor, and upon receipt by the Contractor of the notice the Contract shall be determined but without prejudice to the rights of the parties accrued to the date of determination and to the operation of the following provisions of this Condition.

(2) (a) The Authority shall as soon as practicable, and in any case not later than the expiration of three months from the date of such notice or of the period up to the date for completion, whichever is the shorter, give directions (with which the Contractor shall comply with all reasonable despatch) as to all or any of the following matters–

(i) the performance of further work in accordance with the provisions of the Contract;

(ii) the protection of work executed under the Contract in compliance with directions given under sub-paragraph (i) above;

(iii) the removal from the Site of all things whether or not they were for incorporation;

(iv) the removal of any debris or rubbish and the clearing and making good of the Site;

(v) the termination or transfer of any sub-contracts and contracts (including those for the hire of plant, services and insurance) entered into by the Contractor for the purposes of or in connection with the Contract; or

(vi) any other matter arising out of the Contract with regard to which the Authority (whose decision on the matter shall be final and conclusive) decides that directions are necessary or expedient.

(b) The Authority may at any time within the period referred to in sub-paragraph (a) above by notice to the Contractor vary any direction so given or give fresh directions as to all or any of the matters specified in that sub-paragraph.

(3) (a) In the event of the determination of the Contract under this Condition there shall be paid to the Contractor–

(i) the net amount due, ascertained in the same manner as alterations, additions and omissions under the Contract, in respect of work executed in accordance with the Contract up to the date of determination;

(ii) the net amount due, ascertained in the same manner, in respect of any works or services executed in compliance with directions given by the Authority under paragraph 2(a)(i), (ii), (iii), (except in so far as it relates to things which were for incorporation being things which the Contractor elects to retain), (iv) and (vi) of this Condition;

(iii) the net amount due on the basis of fair and reasonable prices for any things for incorporation which the Contractor, with the consent of the Authorty, has elected not to retain as his own property and which at the date of determination–

    (*a*) had been supplied by the Contractor and properly brought on the Site by him and at his expense in connection with and for the purpose of the Contract, but had not been incorporated in the Works; or

    (*b*) were in course of manufacture by the Contractor in connection with and for the purposes of the Contract and were not lost or damaged by reason of any of the accepted risks; and

(iv) any sum expended by the Contractor on account of the determination of the Contract in respect of the uncompleted portion of any sub-contract and contracts (including those for the hire of plant, services and insurance) entered into by the Contractor for the purposes of or in connection with the Contract, to the extent to which it is reasonable and proper that the Authority should reimburse that sum; and

(v) any sum expended by the Contractor in respect of any contract of employment which is expended on account of the determination of the Contract or which, but for this provision, would represent an unavoidable loss by reason of the determination, to the extent to which it is reasonable and proper that the Authority should reimburse that sum.

(b) If the Works or any part thereof or any things to which sub-paragraph (a)(iii)(*a*) above relates are at the date of determination, or if directions are given in pursuance of paragraph (2)(a) of this Condition at the date for completion of the Works, lost or damaged by reason of any of the accepted risks and such loss or damage was not occasioned by any failure on the part of the Contractor to perform his obligations under Condition 25, the net amount due shall be ascertained as if no loss or damage had occurred.

(c) There shall be deducted from any sum payable to the Contractor under this paragraph the amount of all payments previously made to the Contractor in respect of the Contract, and the Authority shall have the right to retain any reserves accumulated in his possession at the date of determination until the final settlement of all claims made by the Contractor under this paragraph.

(d) The Contractor shall for the purposes of this paragraph keep such wagebooks, time-sheets, books of account and other documents as are necessary to ascertain the sums payable hereunder and shall at the request of the Authority provide (verified in such manner as he may require) any documents so kept and such other information as he may reasonably require in connection with matters arising out of this Condition.

(4) All things not for incorporation which are brought on the Site at the Contractor's expense shall (whether damaged or not) re-vest in and be removed by him as and when they cease to be required in connection with the directions given by the Authority under paragraphs (2)(a)(i), (ii), (iii), (iv) and (vi) of this Condition. The Authority shall be under no liability to the Contractor in respect of the loss thereof or damage thereto caused by reason of any of the accepted risks.

(5) If upon the determination of the Contract under this Condition the Contractor is of the opinion that he has suffered hardship by reason of the operation of this Condition he may refer the circumstances to the Authority, who, on being satisfied that such hardship exists, or has existed, shall make such allowance, if any, as in his opinion is reasonable, and his decision on that matter shall be final and conclusive.

(6) The Contractor shall, in any substantial sub-contract or contract made by him in connection with or for the purposes of the Contract, take power to determine such sub-contract or contract in the event of the determination of the Contract by the Authority upon terms similar to the terms of this Condition, save that the name of the Contractor shall be substituted for the Authority throughout except in paragraphs (3)(a)(iii), (3)(d) and (5).

**Determination of Contract due to default or failure of Contractor**
**45** The Authority may without prejudice to the provisions contained in Condition 46 and without prejudice to his rights against the Contractor in respect of any delay or inferior workmanship or otherwise, or to any claim for damage in respect of any breaches of the Contract and whether the date for completion has or has not elapsed, by notice absolutely determine the Contract in any of the following cases, additional to those mentioned in Condition 55 hereof:
  (a) if the Contractor, having been given by the SO a notice to rectify, reconstruct or replace any defective work or a notice that the work is being performed in an inefficient or otherwise improper manner, shall fail to comply with the requirements of such notice within seven days from the service thereof, or if the Contractor shall delay or suspend the execution of the Works so that either in the judgment of the SO he will be unable to secure the completion of the Works by the date for completion or he has already failed to complete the Works by that date;
  (b)  (i) if the Contractor, being an individual, or where the Contractor is a firm, any partner in that firm, shall at any time become bankrupt, or shall have a receiving order or administration order made against him or shall make any composition or arrangement with or for the benefit of his creditors, or shall make any conveyance or assignment for the benefit of his creditors, or shall purport to do so, or if in Scotland he shall become insolvent or notour bankrupt, or any application shall be made under any Bankruptcy Act for the time being in force for sequestration of his estate, or a trust deed shall be granted by him for behoof of his creditors; or
      (ii) if the Contractor, being a company, shall pass a resolution, or if the

Court shall make an order, that the company shall be wound up, or if the Contractor shall make an arrangement with his creditors or if a receiver or manager on behalf of a creditor shall be appointed, or if circumstances shall arise which entitle the Court or a creditor to appoint a receiver or manager or which entitle the Court to make a winding-up order; or

(c) in a case where the Contractor has failed to comply with Condition 56, if the Authority (whose decision on this matter shall be final and conclusive) shall decide that such failure is prejudicial to the interests of the State:

Provided that such determination shall not prejudice or affect any right of action or remedy which shall have accrued or shall accrue thereafter to the Authority.

## Provisions in case of determination of Contract

**46** (1) If the Authority, in the exercise of the power contained in Conditions 45 or 55, shall determine the Contract, the following provisions shall take effect:

(a) all sums of money that may then be due or accruing due from the Authority to the Contractor shall cease to be due or to accrue due;

(b) the Authority may hire any persons in the employment of the Contractor and with them and/or any other persons provided by the Authority may enter upon and take possession of the Site and of all things (whether or not for incorporation) which are on the Site, and may purchase or do anything requisite for the completion of the Works, or may employ other contractors to complete the same, and the Contractor shall have no claim whatsoever in respect of such action by the Authority;

(c) the Contractor shall (except where determination occurs by reason of any of the circumstances described in Condition 45(b)(i) and (ii)), if required by the Authority, assign to the Authority without further payment, the benefit of any sub-contract or contract for the supply of any things for incorporation which he may have made in connection with the Contract and the Authority shall pay to any such sub-contractor or supplier the price (or the balance thereof remaining unpaid) which the Contractor may have agreed to pay thereunder:

Provided that any part of the price (or balance) so paid which the SO has certified as having been covered by any previous advance shall be forthwith recoverable by the Authority from the Contractor;

(d) notwithstanding that the Authority has not required assignment in accordance with sub-paragraph (c) above the Authority may pay to any nominated sub-contractor or nominated supplier any amount due to him which the SO has certified as having been covered by any previous advance and the amount so paid shall be forthwith recoverable by the Authority from the Contractor; and

(e) the SO shall certify the cost of completion, which shall include–

(i) the cost of any labour or things (whether or not for incorporation) provided to secure completion of the Works, including the making good of any defects and/or faulty work, together with the addition of such percentage to cover superintendence and establishment charges as may be decided by the Authority (whose decision on that matter shall be final and conclusive);

> (ii) the cost of work executed by other contractors to secure completion of the Works, including the making good of any defects and/or faulty work; and
> (iii) the amount of liquidated damages which may under Condition 29 have become due from the Contractor at the date of determination in respect of any delay in the completion of the Works.

(2) If the cost of completion, after taking into account all credits from any sales of any things (whether or not for incorporation) brought on the Site by the Contractor prior to the date of determination, added to the actual sums paid to the Contractor up to the said date, is less than the sum which would have been payable to the Contractor for due completion, the Contractor shall be paid the difference, but the amount so payable shall not exceed the aggregate of–

> (i) the value of the work executed up to the date of determination;
> (ii) the value of any of such things (being things which were for incorporation) as are subsequently incorporated in the Works or otherwise disposed of; and
> (iii) the value of any such things (being things which are not for incorporation) which are disposed of;

less the amount already paid under the Contract. Any such things as are unsold or unused when the Works are completed shall be returned to the Contractor.

(3) If the cost of completion, added to the sum actually paid to the Contractor up to the date of completion, exceeds the sum which would have been payable to the Contractor for due completion, the Authority may apply the proceeds of the sale of any things (whether or not for incorporation) which are on the Site in reduction of such excess and any deficit shall be recoverable from the Contractor. If after such excess has been met there remains any residue of the proceeds of the sale of any such things, and/or any such things remain unsold, such residue or (as the case may be) such things unsold shall be paid or returned to the Contractor.

**Injury to persons: Loss of property**

47 (1) The Condition applies to any personal injury or loss of property (not being a loss of property to which Condition 26 applies) which arises out of or in any way in connection with the execution or purported execution of the Contract.

(2) Subject to the following provisions of this Condition, the Contractor shall–

> (a) be responsible for and reinstate and make good to the satisfaction of the Authority, or make compensation for, any loss of property suffered by the Crown to which this Condition applies;
> (b) indemnify the Crown and servants of the Crown against all claims and proceedings made or brought against the Crown or servants of the Crown in respect of any personal injury or loss of property to which this Condition applies and against all costs and expenses reasonably incurred in connection therewith;
> (c) indemnify the Crown against any payment by the Crown in order to indemnify in whole or in part a servant of the Crown against any such claim, proceedings, costs or expenses; and
> (d) indemnify the Crown against any payment by the Crown to a Crown servant in respect of loss of property to which this Condition applies

suffered by that servant of the Crown and against any payment made under any Government provision in connection with any personal injury to which this Condition applies suffered by any servant of the Crown.

(3) If the Contractor shows that any personal injury or loss of property to which this Condition applies was not caused nor contributed to by his neglect or default or by that of his servants, agents or sub-contractors, or by any circumstances within his or their control, he shall be under no liability under this Condition, and if he shows that the neglect or default of any other person (not being his servant, agent or sub-contractor) was in part responsible for any personal injury or loss of property to which this Condition applies, the Contractor's liability under this Condition shall not extend to the share in the responsibility attributable to the neglect or default of that person.

(4) (a) The Authority shall notify the Contractor of any claim or proceeding made or brought in respect of any personal injury or loss of property to which this Condition applies.

(b) If the Contractor admits that he is liable wholly to indemnify the Crown in respect of any such claim or proceeding, and the claim or proceeding is not an excepted claim, he, or, if he so desires, his insurers, shall be responsible (subject to the condition imposed by the following sub-paragraph) for dealing with or settling that claim or proceeding.

(c) If in connection with any such claim or proceeding with which the Contractor or his insurers are dealing, any matter or issue shall arise which involves or may involve any privilege or special right of the Crown (including any privilege or right in relation to the discovery or production of documents) the Contractor or his insurers shall before taking any action thereon, consult the legal adviser to the Authority and act in relation thereto as may be required by the Authority, and if either the Contractor or his insurers fail to comply with this sub-paragraph, sub-paragraph (b) above shall cease to apply.

(d) For the purposes of the paragraph 'an excepted claim' means a claim or proceeding in respect of a matter falling to be dealt with under a Government provision, or a claim or proceeding made or brought by or against a servant of the Crown.

(5) Where any such claim or proceeding as is mentioned in paragraph (2)(b) or (c) of this Condition is settled otherwise than by the Contractor or his insurers, he shall not be required to pay by way of indemnity any sum greater than that which would be reasonably payable in settlement having regard to the circumstances of the case and in particular to the damages which might be recoverable at law.

(6) In this Condition–

(a) the expression 'loss of property' includes damage to property, loss of profits and loss of use;

(b) the expression 'personal injury' includes sickness and death;

(c) the expressions 'servant of the Crown' and 'servants of the Crown' include persons who are servants of the Crown at the time when a personal injury or loss of property to which this Condition applies occurs, notwithstanding that they cease to be such before any payment in respect of the personal injury or loss of property is made, and, where they have ceased to be such by reason of their deaths, include their personal representatives; and

(d) the expression 'Government provision' means any statute, warrant, order scheme, regulations or conditions of service applicable to a servant of th Crown making provision for continuance of pay or for payment of sic pay, or any allowance to or for the benefit of servants of the Crown, o their families, or dependants during or in respect of sickness, injury o disablement suffered by such servants.

## Damage to public roads

**48** (1) Notwithstanding the provisions of Condition 47, the Authority shall, subject to the following provisions of this Condition, indemnify the Contractor against all claims and proceedings made or brought against the Contractor in respect of an damage to highways, roads or bridges communicating with or on the routes to the Site, including any mains, pipes or cables under such highways, roads or bridges caused by any extraordinary traffic of the Contractor or a sub-contractor o supplier in connection with the Works.

(2) The Contractor shall take all reasonable steps to prevent such highways, road and bridges from being subjected to damage by extraordinary traffic as aforesaid and in particular but without prejudice to the generality of the foregoing shall select routes, choose and use vehicles and restrict and distribute loads so that any such extraordinary traffic shall be limited so far as is reasonably practicable.

(3) The Contractor shall, without prejudice to his obligations under paragraph (2 of this Condition, comply with such instructions regarding any of the matter mentioned in the said paragraph as may be given to him from time to time in writing by the SO.

(4) The Contractor shall notify the Authority of any claim or proceeding made o brought in respect of any damage to highways, roads or bridges by extraordinary traffic to which this Condition applies and thereafter the Authority shall be responsible for dealing with or settling that claim or proceeding:

Provided always that if it is decided by the Authority that any such claim o proceeding is due, wholly or in part, to any failure by the Contractor to comply with the provisions of paragraph (2) of this Condition or with the SO's instruction under paragraph (3) thereof, then the Authority may recover from the Contractor so much of the costs and expenses incurred by the Authority in connection with such claim or proceeding, as is due to the failure of the Contractor in that respect

(5) 'Extraordinary traffic' for the purpose of this Condition means extraordinary traffic to which Section 62 of the Highways Act 1959, (or in relation to Scotland Section 54 of the Road Traffic Act 1930) or any statutory modification o re-enactment thereof as for the time being in force, applies.

## Emergency powers

**49** If in the opinion of the SO any urgent measures shall become necessary during the progress of the execution of the Works to obviate any risk of accident or failure, o if, by reason of the happening of any accident or failure, or other event in connection with the execution of the Works, any remedial or other work or repair shall become urgently necessary for security and the Contractor be unable o unwilling at once to carry out such measures or work or repair, the Authority may by his own or other workpeople carry out such measures or execute such work or repair as the SO may consider necessary. If the measures carried out or the work or repair so executed by the Authority shall be such as the Contractor is liable under the Contract to carry out or execute at his own expense all costs and expenses so incurred by the Authority shall be recoverable from the Contractor.

**Facilities for other works**

**50** The Authority shall have power at any time to execute other works (whether or not in connection with the Works) on the Site contemporaneously with the execution of the Works and the Contractor shall give reasonable facilities for such purpose:

Provided that the Contractor shall not be responsible for damage done to such other works except in so far as such damage has been caused by the negligence, omission or default of his workpeople or agents; and any damage done to the Works in the execution of such other works shall, for the purpose of Condition 26(2), be deemed to be damage which is wholly caused by the neglect or default of a servant of the Crown acting in the course of his employment as such.

**Fair wages, etc**

**51** The Contractor shall, in the execution of the Contract, observe and fulfil the obligations upon contractors specified in the Fair Wages Resolution passed by the House of Commons on 14 October, 1946, namely:

(1) (a) The contractor shall pay rates of wages and observe hours and conditions of labour not less favourable than those established for the trade or industry in the district where the work is carried out by machinery of negotiation or arbitration to which the parties are organizations of employers and trade unions representative respectively of substantial proportions of the employers and workers engaged in the trade or industry in the district.

   (b) In the absence of any rates of wages, hours or conditions of labour so established the contractor shall pay rates of wages and observe hours and conditions of labour which are not less favourable than the general level of wages, hours and conditions observed by other employers whose general circumstances in the trade or industry in which the contractor is engaged are similar.

(2) The contractor shall in respect of all persons employed by him (whether in execution of the contract or otherwise) in every factory, workshop or place occupied or used by him for the execution of the contract comply with the general conditions required by this Resolution. Before a contractor is placed upon a Department's lists of firms to be invited to tender, the Department shall obtain from him an assurance that to the best of his knowledge and belief he has complied with the general conditions required by this Resolution for at least the previous three months.

(3) In the event of any question arising as to whether the requirements of this Resolution are being observed, the question shall, if not otherwise disposed of, be referred by the Minister of Labour and National Service to an independent Tribunal for decision.

(4) The contractor shall recognize the freedom of his workpeople to be members of trade unions.

(5) The contractor shall at all times during the continuance of a contract display, for the information of his workpeople, in every factory, workshop or place occupied or used by him for the execution of the contract a copy of this Resolution.

(6) The contractor shall be responsible for the observance of this Resolution by sub-contractors employed in the execution of the contract, and shall if required notify the Department of the names and addresses of all such sub-contractors.

*Note:* Copies of the Resolution may be purchased from HM Stationery Office.

### Racial discrimination

**52** (1) The Contractor shall not unlawfully discriminate within the meaning and scope of the provisions of the Race Relations Act 1968 or any statutory modification or re-enactment thereof relating to discrimination in employment.

(2) The Contractor shall take all reasonable steps to ensure the observance of the provisions of paragraph (1) of this Condition by all servants, employees or agents of the Contractor and all sub-contractors.

*Note:* Contractors will be aware that the Race Relations Act 1968 does not apply in Northern Ireland but attention is drawn to paragraph (2) above which will be relevant in the case of sub-contractors in other parts of the United Kingdom.

### Prolongation and disruption expenses

**53** (1) If–
    (a) complying with any of the SO's instructions;
    (b) the making good of loss or damage falling within Condition 26(2);
    (c) the execution of works pursuant to Condition 50; or
    (d) delay in the provision of any of the items specified in paragraph (2) of this Condition

unavoidably results in the regular progress of the Works or of any part thereof being materially disrupted or prolonged and in consequence of such disruption or prolongation the Contractor properly and directly incurs any expense in performing the Contract which he would not otherwise have incurred and which is beyond that otherwise provided for in or reasonably contemplated by the Contract, the Contract Sum shall, subject to paragraph (3) of this Condition and to Condition 23, be increased by the amount of that expense as ascertained by the Quantity Surveyor:

Provided that there shall be no such increase in respect of expense incurred in consequence of the making good of loss or damage falling within Condition 26(2) except where the Contractor is entitled to payment under that provision, and where his entitlement to payment under that provision is limited to a proportionate sum any such increase in respect of expense so incurred shall be limited in like manner.

(2) The items referred to in sub-paragraph (1)(d) of this Condition are–
    (a) any drawings, schedules, levels or other design information to be provided

by the SO and to be prepared otherwise than by the Contractor or any of his sub-contractors;

(b) any work the execution of which, or thing the supplying of which, is to be undertaken by the Authority or is to be ordered direct by him otherwise than from the Contractor and is to be so undertaken or ordered otherwise than in consequence of any default on the part of the Contractor; and

(c) any direction from the Authority or the SO regarding the nomination or appointment of any person, or any instruction of the SO or consent of the Authority, to be given under Condition 38(4).

(3) It shall be a condition precedent to the Contract Sum being increased under paragraph (1) of this Condition–

(a) in the case of expense incurred in consequence of an SO's instruction, that the instruction shall have been given or confirmed in writing and shall not have been rendered necessary as a result of any default on the part of the Contractor;

(b) in the case of expense incurred in consequence of delay in the provision of any of the items specified in paragraph (2) of this Condition, that, except where a date for the provision of the relevant item was agreed with the SO, the Contractor shall, neither unreasonably early nor unreasonably late, have given notice to the SO specifying that item and the date by which it was reasonably required; and

(c) in any case that–

   (i) the Contractor, immediately upon becoming aware that the regular progress of the Works or of any part thereof has been or is likely to be disrupted or prolonged as aforesaid, shall have given notice to the SO specifying the circumstances causing or expected to cause that disruption or prolongation and stating that he is or expects to be entitled to an increase in the Contract Sum under that paragraph;

   (ii) as soon as reasonably practicable after incurring the expense the Contractor shall have provided such documents and information in respect of the expense as he is required to provide under Condition 37(2).

**Corrupt gifts and payments of commission**

**55** (1) The Contractor shall not–

(a) offer or give or agree to give to any person in Her Majesty's service any gift or consideration of any kind as an inducement or reward for doing or forbearing to do or for having done or forborne to do any act in relation to the obtaining or execution of this or any other contract for Her Majesty's service or for showing or forbearing to show favour or disfavour to any person in relation to this or any other contract for Her Majesty's service; or

(b) enter into this or any other contract with Her Majesty or any Government Department in connection with which commission has been paid or agreed to be paid by him or on his behalf or to his knowledge, unless before the contract is made particulars of any such commission and of the terms and conditions of any agreement for the payment thereof have been disclosed in writing to the Authority.

(2) Any breach of this Condition by the Contractor or by anyone employed by him or acting on his behalf (whether with or without the knowledge of the Contractor) or the commission of any offence by the Contractor or by anyone employed by him or acting on his behalf under the Prevention of Corruption Acts, 1889 to 1916, in relation to this or any other contract for Her Majesty's service shall entitle the Authority to determine the Contract and/or to recover from the Contractor the amount or value of any such gift, consideration or commission.

(3) Any dispute or difference of opinion arising in respect of either the interpretation or effect of this Condition or of the amount recoverable hereunder by the Authority from the Contractor shall be decided by the Authority, whose decision on that matter shall be final and conclusive.

### Admission to the Site

**56** (1) If the Authority gives the Contractor notice that any person is not to be admitted to the Site, the Contractor shall take all reasonable steps to prevent his being admitted.

(2) The Contractor shall take such steps as the SO may reasonably require of him to prevent persons who are aliens, other than citizens of a Member State of the European Economic Community, or who are British subjects by virtue only of certificates of naturalization in which their names were included, being admitted to the Site without the permission in writing of the Authority first having been obtained.

(3) If and when directed by the SO, the Contractor shall furnish a list of the names and addresses of all persons who are or may be at any time concerned with the Works or any part thereof, specifying the capacities in which they are so concerned, and giving such other particulars as the SO may reasonably require.

(4) The decision of the Authority as to whether any person is to be admitted to the Site, and as to whether the Contractor has furnished the information or taken the steps required of him by this Condition shall be final and conclusive.

### Passes

**57** Where, in order to meet the requirements of public policy, public safety or security or public health, passes are required for the admission of workpeople to the Site, the SO shall arrange for their issue to the Contractor, and to the extent required by the SO the Contractor shall submit to the SO a list of the names of the workpeople and produce satisfactory evidence as to their identity and bona fides so that the name on each individual pass can be filled in before the passes are issued. The passes shall be returned at any time on the demand of the SO and in any case on the completion of the Works.

### Photographs

**58** The Contractor shall not at any time take any photograph of the Site or of the Works or of any part thereof, and shall take all reasonable steps to ensure that no such photograph shall at any time be taken or published or otherwise circulated by any person employed by him, unless the Contractor or such person shall first have obtained the permission in writing of the Authority.

**Secrecy**

**59** (1) The Contractor's attention is drawn to the provisions of the Official Secrets Acts 1911 to 1939 and where appropriate, to the provisions of Section 11 of the Atomic Energy Act 1946.

(2) The Contractor shall take all reasonable steps to ensure that all persons employed by him in connection with the Contract are aware that these statutory provisions apply to them during the continuance and after the completion or earlier determination of the Contract.

(3) Information concerning the Contract and any information obtained either by the Contractor in the course of the execution of the Contract or by any person employed by him in connection with the Contract in the course of such employment is confidential and shall be used by the Contractor and by any such person solely for the purpose of the Contract and shall not at any time be disclosed by the Contractor or by any such person without the consent of the Authority except to such persons and to such extent as may be necessary for the execution of the Contract.

**Arbitration**

**61** (1) All disputes, differences or questions between the parties to the Contract with respect to any matter or thing arising out of or relating to the Contract other than a matter or thing arising out of or relating to Condition 51 or as to which the decision or report of the Authority or of any other person is by the Contract expressed to be final and conclusive shall after notice by either party to the Contract to the other of them be referred to a single Arbitrator agreed for that purpose, or in default of such agreement to be appointed at the request of the Authority by the President of such one of the undermentioned as the Authority may decide, viz, the Law Society (or, when appropriate, the Law Society of Scotland), the Royal Institute of British Architects, the Royal Institution of Chartered Surveyors, the Royal Incorporation of Architects in Scotland, the Institutions of Civil Engineers, Mechanical Engineers, Heating and Ventilating Engineers, Electrical Engineers or Structural Engineers.

(2) Unless the parties otherwise agree, such reference shall not take place until after the completion, alleged completion or abandonment of the Works or the determination of the Contract.

(3) In the case of the Contract being subject to English Law such reference shall be deemed to be a submission to arbitration under the Arbitration Act 1950, or any statutory modification or re-enactment thereof.

(4) In the case of the Contract being subject to Scots Law, the Law of Scotland shall apply to the arbitration and the award of the Arbiter, including any award as to the amount of any compensation, damages and expenses to or against any of the parties to the arbitration, shall be final and binding on the parties, provided that at any stage of the arbitration the Arbiter may, and if so requested by either of the parties shall, prepare a statement of facts in a special case for the opinion and judgment of the Court of Session on any question or questions of Law arising in the arbitration, and both parties to the arbitration shall be bound to concur in presenting to the Court a special case in the terms prepared by the Arbiter and in

which the statement of facts prepared by him is agreed to by the parties, with such contentions as the parties or either of them may desire to add thereto for the opinion and judgment of the Court; and the Arbiter and the parties to the arbitration shall be bound by the answer or answers returned by the Court of Session, or if the case is appealed to the House of Lords, by the House, to the question or questions of Law stated in the case.

*Notes*

The following notes indicate the changes from the previous Edition but do not form part of the Contract.

| | | |
|---|---|---|
| Definitions: | Contract Sum | Reference to new Condition 53 added. |
| Condition No. 9 | | Amended Condition. |
| | 5(2), 10, 39 and 40(3) | Reference to Condition 9 amended to 9(1). |
| | 15 | Proviso amended. |
| | 23 | Amended. |
| | 28(2)(*b*) | Amended. |
| | 37 | Heading amended. |
| | 37(2) | Amended. |
| | 40(2) | Reference to '90 per cent' amended to '97 per cent'. |
| | 40 | New sub-paragraph (5). |
| | 40(5) and (6) | Sub-paragraph numbers amended to (6) and (7). |
| | 44(3)(*a*)(iv) | Amended. |
| | 44(3)(*a*)(v) | New sub-paragraph. |
| | 50 | Amended. |
| | 53 | New Condition. |

Amendment Sheet No. 2, which amended '90 per cent' to '97 per cent', has been incorporated in this Edition.

# Appendix D: Definition of prime cost of daywork carried out under a building contract, 2nd edition, 1 December 1975

This Definition of Prime Cost is published by The Royal Institution of Chartered Surveyors and the National Federation of Building Trades Employers, for convenience and for use by people who choose to use it. Members of the National Federation of Building Trades Employers are not in any way debarred from defining Prime Cost and rendering their accounts for work carried out on that basis in any way they choose. Building owners are advised to reach agreement with contractors on the Definition of Prime Cost to be used prior to issuing instructions.

### Section 1    Application

1.1 This definition provides a basis for the valuation of daywork executed under such building contracts as provide for its use (e.g. contracts embodying the Standard Forms issued by the Joint Contracts Tribunal).

1.2 It is not applicable in any other circumstances, such as jobbing or other work carried out as a separate or main contract nor in the case of daywork executed during the Defects Liability Period of contracts embodying the above mentioned Standard Forms.

### Section 2    Composition of Total Charges

2.1 The prime cost of daywork comprises the sum of the following costs:
   (a) Labour as defined in Section 3.
   (b) Materials and goods as defined in Section 4.
   (c) Plant as defined in Section 5.

2.2 Incidental costs, overheads and profit as defined in Section 6, as provided in the building contract and expressed therein as percentage adjustments, are applicable to each of 2.1 (a)–(c).

### Section 3    Labour

3.1 The standard wage rates, emoluments and expenses referred to below and the standard working hours referred to in 3.2 are those laid down for the time being in the rules or decisions of the National Joint Council for the Building Industry and the terms of the Building and Civil Engineering Annual and Public Holiday Agreements applicable to the works, or the rules or decisions or agreements of such body, other than the National Joint Council for the Building Industry, as may be applicable relating to the class of labour concerned at the time when and in the area where the daywork is executed.

3.2 Hourly base rates for labour are computed by dividing the annual prime cost of labour, based upon standard working hours and as defined in 3.4 (a)–(i), by the number of standard working hours per annum (see examples on page 8).

3.3 The hourly rates computed in accordance with 3.2 shall be applied in respect of the time spent by operatives directly engaged on daywork, including those operating mechanical plant and transport and erecting and dismantling other plant (unless otherwise expressly provided in the building contract).

3.4 The annual prime cost of labour comprises the following:
   (a) Guaranteed minimum weekly earnings (e.g. Standard Basic Rate of Wages, Joint Board Supplement and Guaranteed Minimum Bonus Payment in the case of NJCBI rules).
   (b) All other guaranteed minimum payments (unless included in Section 6).
   (c) Differentials or extra payments in respect of skill, responsibility, discomfort, inconvenience or risk (excluding those in respect of supervisory responsibility – see 3.5).
   (d) Payments in respect of public holidays.
   (e) Any amounts which may become payable by the Contractor to or in respect of operatives arising from the operation of the rules referred to in 3.1 which are not provided for in 3.4 (a)–(d) or in Section 6.
   (f) Employer's National Insurance contributions applicable to 3.4 (a)–(e).
   (g) Employer's contributions to annual holiday credits.
   (h) Employer's contributions to death benefit scheme.
   (i) Any contribution, levy or tax imposed by statute, payable by the Contractor in his capacity as an employer.

3.5 **Note:**
   Differentials or extra payments in respect of supervisory responsibility are excluded from the annual prime cost (see Section 6). The time of principals, foremen, gangers, leading hands and similar categories, when working manually, is admissible under this Section at the appropriate rates for the trades concerned.

### Section 4   Materials and Goods

4.1 The prime cost of materials and goods obtained from stockists or manufacturers is the invoice cost after deduction of all trade discounts but including cash discounts not exceeding 5 per cent and includes the cost of delivery to site.

4.2 The prime cost of materials and goods supplied from the Contractor's stock is based upon the current market prices plus any appropriate handling charges.

4.3 Any Value Added Tax which is treated, or is capable of being treated, as input tax (as defined in the Finance Act, 1972) by the Contractor is excluded.

### Section 5   Plant

5.1 The rates for plant shall be as provided in the building contract.

5.2 The costs included in this Section comprise the following:
   (a) Use of mechanical plant and transport for the time employed on daywork.

(b) Use of non-mechanical plant (excluding non-mechanical hand tools) for the time employed on daywork.

5.3 **Note:**
The use of non-mechanical hand tools and of erected scaffolding, staging, trestles or the like is excluded (see Section 6).

**Section 6   Incidental Costs, Overheads and Profit**

6.1 The percentage adjustments provided in the building contract, which are applicable to each of the totals of Sections 3, 4 and 5, comprise the following:
(a) Head Office charges.
(b) Site staff including site supervision.
(c) The additional cost of overtime (other than that referred to in 6.2).
(d) Time lost due to inclement weather.
(e) The additional cost of bonuses and all other incentive payments in excess of any guaranteed minimum included in 3.4 (a).
(f) Apprentices study time.
(g) Subsistence and periodic allowances.
(h) Fares and travelling allowances.
(i) Sick pay or insurance in respect thereof.
(j) Third party and employer's liability insurance.
(k) Liability in respect of redundancy payments to employees.
(l) Employer's National Insurance contributions not included in Section 3.4.
(m) Tool allowances.
(n) Use, repair and sharpening of non-mechanical hand tools.
(o) Use of erected scaffolding, staging, trestles or the like.
(p) Use of tarpaulins, protective clothing, artificial lighting, safety and welfare facilities, storage and the like that may be available on the site.
(q) Any variation to basic rates required by the Contractor in cases where the building contract provides for the use of a specified schedule of basic plant charges (to the extent that no other provision is made for such variation).
(r) All other liabilities and obligations whatsoever not specifically referred to in this Section nor chargeable under any other section.
(s) Profit.

6.2 **Note:**

The additional cost of overtime, where specifically ordered by the Architect/Supervising Officer, shall only be chargeable in the terms of prior written agreement between the parties to the building contract.

Example of calculation of typical standard hourly base rate (as defined in Section 3) for NJCBI building craft operative and labourer in Grade A areas based upon rates ruling at 1st July 1975.

| | Rate | Craft operative | Rate | Labourer |
|---|---|---|---|---|
| | £ | £ | £ | £ |
| Guaranteed minimum weekly earnings | | | | |
| Standard Basic Rate | 49 wks  37.00 | 1,813.00 | 31.40 | 1,538.60 |
| Joint Board Supplement | 49 wks  5.00 | 245.00 | 4.20 | 205.80 |
| Guaranteed Minimum Bonus | 49 wks  4.00 | 196.00 | 3.60 | 176.40 |
| | | 2,254.00 | | 1,920.80 |
| Employer' National Insurance Contribution at 8.5% | | 191.59 | | 163.27 |
| | | 2,445.59 | | 2,084.07 |
| Employer's Contributions to: | | | | |
| CITB annual levy | | 15.00 | | 3.00 |
| Annual holiday credits | 49 wks  2.80 | 137.20 | 2.80 | 137.20 |
| Public holidays (included in guaranteed minimum weekly earnings above) | | — | | — |
| Death benefit scheme | 49 wks  0.10 | 4.90 | 0.10 | 4.90 |
| Annual labour cost as defined in Section 3 | | £2,602.69 | | £2,229.17 |

Hourly base rates as defined       *Craft operative*                                      *Labourer*
in Section 3, clause 3.2         $\dfrac{£2602.69}{1904} = £1.37$   $\dfrac{£2229.17}{1904} =$  £1.17

*Note:* (1)   Standard working hours per annum calculated as follows:

|  |  |  |
|---|---|---|
| 52 weeks @ 40 hours = | | 2080 |
| *Less* | | |
| 3 weeks holiday @ 40 hours = | 120 | |
| 7 days public holidays @ 8 hours = | 56 | 176 |
| | | 1904 |

(2)   It should be noted that all labour costs incurred by the Contractor in his capacity as an employer, other than those contained in the hourly base rate, are to be taken into account under Section 6.

(3)   The above example is for the convenience of users only and does not form part of the Definition; all the basic costs are subject to re-examination according to the time when and in the area where the daywork is executed.